Of America II

Fourth Edition

A Beka Book® Pensacola, FL 32523-9100
an affiliate of PENSACOLA CHRISTIAN COLLEGE®

To Parents and Teachers

Students are eagerly searching for a workable sense of values. They need reading material that will give them ideals to reach for and examples to follow.

The stories in this reader have been selected from the readers of America's past and have been edited, modernized, and classroom-tested for student appeal and readability. Many character values are woven throughout the stories. Thought questions at the end of the stories aid in understanding the selections.

Of America II
Fourth Edition

Staff Credits
Compiled by: Beverly Rainey, Phyllis Rand
Managing Editor: Corinne Sawtelle
Editorial Staff: Marion Hedquist
Designer: Michelle Johnson
Illustrators: Brian Jekel; Dan Weller, and staff

Copyright © mmx, mmi, mcmlxxxvii, mcmlxxv   Pensacola Christian College
All rights reserved. Printed in U.S.A.

Credits are found on pp. 308–309 which are an extension of this page.

No part of this publication may be reproduced or transmitted in any form or by any means, electronic or mechanical, including photocopy, recording, or any information storage and retrieval system, or by license from any collective or licensing body, without permission in writing from the publisher.

A Beka Book, a Christian textbook ministry affiliated with Pensacola Christian College, is designed to meet the need for Christian textbooks and teaching aids. The purpose of this publishing ministry is to help Christian schools reach children and young people for the Lord and train them in the Christian way of life.

Cataloging Data
        Of America II / ed. Beverly Rainey, Phyllis
    Rand—4th edition
    --p. : col. ill. ; 23 cm. (A Beka Book reading
    program)
        1. Readers (Elementary) 2. Reading
(Elementary) III. A Beka Book, Inc.
Library Congress: PE1119 .04 2010
Dewey System: 428.6

CONTENTS

*This story could be read during black history month.

America My Home

Stories and People Americans Love

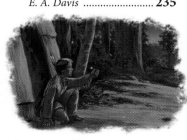

*This poem could be read during black history month.

A National Prayer

Thomas Jefferson

Almighty God, Who has given us this good land for our heritage; we humbly beseech Thee that we may always prove ourselves a people mindful of Thy favor and glad to do Thy will. Bless our land with honorable industry, sound learning, and pure manners.

Save us from violence, discord, and confusion, from pride and arrogance, and from every evil way. Defend our liberties, and fashion into one united people the multitude brought hither out of many kindreds and tongues.

Endow with the spirit of wisdom those to whom in Thy Name we entrust the authority of government, that there may be justice and peace at home, and that through obedience to Thy law, we may show forth Thy praise among the nations of the earth.

In time of prosperity, fill our hearts with thankfulness, and, in the day of trouble, suffer not our trust in Thee to fail; all of which we ask through Jesus Christ our Lord. AMEN.

Success

Henry Wadsworth Longfellow

We have not wings, we cannot soar;
   But we have feet to scale and climb
By slow degrees, by more and more,
   The cloudy summits of our time.

The mighty pyramids of stone
   That wedge-like cleave the desert airs,
When nearer seen, and better known,
   Are but gigantic flights of stairs.

The distant mountains, that uprear
   Their solid bastions to the skies.
Are crossed by pathways, that appear
   As we to higher levels rise.

The heights by great men reached and kept
   Were not attained by sudden flight,
But they, while their companions slept,
   Were toiling upward in the night.

---

cleave—*pierce, split apart*

A Precious Gift:
The Work of Dr. Charles Drew

Rhoda Truax

Dr. Charles R. Drew, Medical Supervisor of Blood for Britain—a project for supplying blood plasma to Great Britain in World War II—paused for a moment to look in on the first important step of his new undertaking. This was the giving of blood. The project Dr. Drew was supervising was the first of its kind. It would serve as a model for other cities and, with modification, for the armed services and hospitals. Dr. Drew was constantly on the alert for ways to improve techniques.

The blood donor he was watching lay on his back on a cot. His left arm was connected by a tube to a bottle standing on a little table by his head.

---

plasma—*the clear liquid part of blood that cells float in*
modification—*alteration; change*

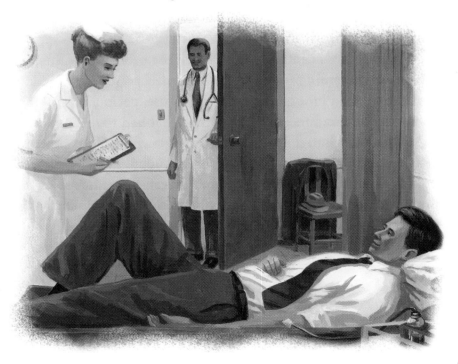

"Everything's all right, isn't it?" the man asked as the nurse came over to him, his voice a shade too casual.

"Everything's just fine, Mr. Osgood," the nurse said to him.

The nurse's manner, Dr. Drew observed, was excellent, as was that of all the nurses and doctors who were volunteering their services. They were matter-of-fact, as though this was a simple routine affair, as, indeed, it was. Yet they conveyed the impression that the donors were doing something admirable, and this was also true. It was important to treat the donors properly. No stirring appeals for volunteers could be so effective as word-of-mouth reports by those who had given blood without finding the process unpleasant.

The response of volunteers was more than gratifying. The first blood for the project had been collected from doctors and nurses on August 16, 1940, the day the bombing of London began. Within a month, mainly because of appeals to churches, synagogues, and various organizations, 1,723 people had given blood. Early in September the aerial blitzkrieg against London had begun, and by October 26 there had been 8,699 donors. The number was steadily increasing.

This was excellent, but it increased the problems of the project and its director. More workers were needed to take the blood, to make tests, to process the blood, to bottle, pack, and ship it. Each step was crammed with questions that had to be answered.

Which was safest and most practical—whole blood, serum, or plasma? Should plasma, once decided upon, be dried or sent in fluid form? Should the white and red cells be removed by the slow method of letting them settle to the bottom? Or by the faster and more expensive method of using a centrifuge? What were the best methods of testing for infected blood before pooling it?

---

conveyed—*communicated*
blitzkrieg—*a sudden military attack from the air*

serum—*a yellowish fluid found in blood*
centrifuge—*a device that separates liquids by spinning so the heavier one goes to the outside*

These and many, many other questions had to be answered at the same time that large quantities of safe plasma were being sent to England. Dr. Drew, who was a research scientist as well as a surgeon, mourned because there was not time to investigate all the possibilities of this tremendous project.

But now the nurse was speaking again to the blood donor Dr. Drew had been watching. He turned his attention back to her.

"We've almost finished, Mr. Osgood," she said. "Just lie still a few minutes, please."

Mr. Osgood was apparently not inclined to follow instructions. He sat up quickly and turned his head to look at the flask that the nurse was placing on a rack. "Well, what do you know! Did I give all that?" he asked. The question began in a booming voice but trailed off. The nurse caught him as he was about to fall back, and she eased his head on the cot again. Without appearing to hurry, the Doctor brought the smelling salts.

"I don't know what got into me," the man said after a minute or two. "I never passed out in my life."

"I'm afraid you sat up a little too suddenly," the nurse told him. "And besides, it's often the huskiest men who get upset at the sight of blood. We had one in here the other day who was an all-American football player. He fainted dead away."

It was always difficult for Dr. Drew to realize that many people reacted with horror at the very thought of blood. He found everything about it fascinating: its physical and chemical composition; the way it wound through the entire body in about a minute, its red cells carrying oxygen to all the tissues; the way the white cells and plasma protected the body against infection.

Yet in spite of all that is known about blood, superstitions persist. "It's in his blood to act that way," people remark. They explain differences between people by supposed differences in their blood.

It is true that the blood of all individuals is not alike. There are four different types, and the differences can be very important; but they have nothing to do with racial, religious, or national groupings. Each of the four  blood types includes people of all colors and nationalities. The blood of a Norwegian can differ from that of his own relatives and "match" that of a Japanese or an Indian.

It was strange, Dr. Drew thought, that people could know this scientific fact and yet continue to talk about "Jewish blood" or "colored blood." He realized that a great many of his fellow citizens would not want to accept a transfusion of his blood because he was African-American.

As a surgeon, Dr. Drew was particularly interested in transfusions as a means of preventing and treating the condition known as shock. Following a serious operation or injury, a patient's blood pressure would often drop. His pulse would become weak and his skin cold and clammy. He would collapse and perhaps die. A transfusion could work wonders in such a case.

Dr. Drew had been interested in blood research for a number of years. In 1938 he was engaged in blood research at Columbia University. Two years later his thesis, *Banked Blood,* was published.

There could have been no more timely subject. World War II had broken out. Some of the nations, recognizing the importance of transfusions to the wounded, had established some mobile units to collect blood and others to give transfusions.

---

thesis—*a long essay proving an idea*

The British lost most of their units in the retreat at Dunkirk. Their situation was now critical, as was that of France, Belgium, and Holland.

As the need for help grew more and more desperate, the Blood for Britain project was planned and formed in New York. Dr. Drew, who was then teaching at Howard University, was asked to serve as full-time director. He was, the board felt, "best qualified of anyone we know to act in this important development . . . a recognized authority on the subject of blood preservation."

Dr. Drew would have preferred staying at Howard University, teaching black medical students. He loved surgery, and he felt that his people needed him. On the other hand, an African-American in such an important position could help in the struggle against prejudice and discrimination.

Charles Drew knew well what prejudice was. As a student he had heard the crowds cheer for him and three other black students on the track team as they piled up crucial points in a meet. After the cheers had died away, an embarrassing situation had arisen in connection with a banquet for the track team: no large hotel could be found that was willing to serve black athletes. Would they mind, they were asked, eating by themselves at the college? If Dr. Drew should ever be tempted to believe that applause made him special, he would hear in his memory the words "Would you mind. . . ?" as they hung over the table where four members of the team sat by themselves in absolute silence.

But he had other reasons for accepting the position. It would enable him to help win the war and to save lives. Lives were already being saved. Dr. Drew wished that every adult could see a transfusion. Then more people would donate blood to fill the needs of peace as well as war. Perhaps the old feelings

---

crucial—*extremely important*

about blood would change. A man might look at a total stranger and say to himself: Maybe my blood is flowing in his veins.

The night after Mr. Osgood gave his blood, a storm blanketed the British coast. Enemy aircraft were all grounded, and the tired people of London hoped for a good night's rest.

Shortly before dawn, however, the clouds lifted and the German planes crossed the Channel in a great wave. Warning signals of a raid were unheeded by people who were too drugged by sleep to hurry to shelters.

Most of the bombs fell on the poorest sections of London. One of them scored a direct hit on an old three-story building not far from the Thames River.

Alec Macintosh lived on the ground floor with his daughter and his daughter-in-law and her baby. He had been awake, for who could sleep through the screaming of the sirens, the anti-aircraft fire, and the bombs?

After the explosion he was out on the street, surrounded by the wreckage of his home, staring up at the sky that was criss-crossed by the probing fingers of searchlights.

Air Raid Precaution workers and neighbors moved hurriedly around him.

"Rose is inside!" he cried suddenly. "Rose and the baby. Sarah's working the night shift, but Rose and the baby are inside. You've got to get them out."

"Easy now, mate," a rescue worker told him. Then the worker turned to some young men and said, "Lend a hand here, lads. A woman and child are inside."

A woman neighbor, carrying a bucket of sand, called out, "It's Tom's wife. She's in there somewhere."

"Let me help," Alec cried. "I'm all right now."

"Well, then, we can use a hand. Hold that beam while I set a prop here," someone directed.

The wavering glow from the searchlights came through a gaping hole in the ceiling. It revealed something white under the wreckage—a woman and a child. In a few minutes the men got them out, and then, in a lull, they heard the baby cry. The child was uninjured, having been protected by her mother's body.

"I'll take the baby. It's me, Lizzie Wells, and I'll take care of the poor little thing," said a neighbor.

Alec nodded, wondering who would take care of the baby later, with no mother and with Tom in the hospital since Dunkirk, where he had lost a leg. Alec was sure Rose was dead, for he had touched her hand and found it cold and clammy.

"Make way for the nurse."

A nurse knelt down beside Rose Macintosh. Sharply she gave orders. "This girl's alive. Fetch the doctor at once. He's down by the corner."

Within a few minutes the doctor had taken over. Alec stood with a hooded flashlight, directing its beam on the ground where Rose lay covered. The doctor stopped the bleeding from the gash in her arm. Now he inserted into her other arm a needle to which a tube was connected.

He stood up, raising his hand to hold up something to which the tube was attached. Alec saw that it was a bottle of colorless fluid.

When the flask was empty, the doctor said, "That's it," and knelt beside the young mother. Alec could scarcely believe it, but Rose's face had changed. There was a little color in it, and her eyelids fluttered.

"My baby . . . my baby."

"Your baby is safe. And you'll be all right soon, too." The doctor turned to Alec. "Keep her quiet and warm until the stretcher-bearers come and take her to the hospital. Bad case of shock, but the plasma picked her up."

"Plasma?"

"Blood plasma from the United States," the doctor said. "It's coming in regularly now, and they say we can count on an increased supply. Makes all the difference on a night like this."

Close by there was the explosion of another bomb. There's all kinds of people, Alec told himself. Those that drop bombs on us who never did them any harm, and those who send us their own blood. He looked down at the shadows where his son's wife lay, wondering who it could have been that saved her life. Whoever it was, he thought, I wish I could shake his hand and thank him and call him brother.

In 1950 the following notice appeared in a magazine.

DIED. Dr. Charles Richard Drew, 45, pioneer in the collection and use of blood plasma. . . . For supervising New York's blood donations to bombed Britain and directing the first Red Cross collection unit for the United States armed forces, he won the 1943 Spingarn Award for the highest achievement by an American Negro.

Character Theme—Perseverance & Service

Time to Think

1. Dr. Charles Drew was an expert in what field?
2. Dr. Drew loved teaching. Why did he leave his position at Howard University to become director of Blood for Britain?
3. What saved Rose's life?
4. How old was Dr. Drew when he died?

*God grants liberty only to those who love it
and are always ready to guard it and defend it.*
—Daniel Webster

Heroism

Angelo Patri

In the 1920s, when this essay was written, Americans expected their political leaders to be people of high integrity. They knew that "righteousness exalteth a nation: but sin is a reproach to any people" (Prov. 14:34). If we would enjoy God's blessing on our nation in this new millennium, it is time to sound the trumpet once more for righteousness.

It takes a brave soul to stand alone and hold up the standard of an unpopular cause. That is the true type of courage, rare courage. There is plenty of the cat and dog courage. Any animal will bite and scratch and claw an enemy, but the higher quality of courage does not come so easily. It has to be trained into us. It must be practiced day by day. It will not come of itself. It is born of a strong will and a willingness to sacrifice.

We laugh at the story of George Washington and his hatchet, but it is really one of the traditions of American life. It stands for our idea of courage. We like it even though we smile at it. America dare not lie. We insist that our relations with other countries shall be open and straightforward. We believe in the open treaties openly arrived at. Secrecy, plotting against another, diplomatic bargainings are not palatable to the American people. But it takes tremendous courage to hold to this tradition and carry it on. Our political leaders must be made of stern stuff if they would live up to it. Yet again and again Americans have lived up to it.

Would we stand up and be counted for the cause we believe in even though we knew that doing so meant the loss of friends and money and position?

palatable—*acceptable*

12

Could we make a great sacrifice for the good of humanity even though we knew our only reward would be the doubtful gratitude of the people we helped or a line on a lonely monument a hundred years after death?

If we could and if we did, we should be the true type of American hero.

Character Theme—Courage, Honesty, & Honor

Time to Think

1. What are some causes for which we must stand up and be counted?
2. Name some people who made a great sacrifice for the good of humanity.
3. Who are your heroes? Do they possess the higher quality of courage described here?
4. Memorize the quotation by Daniel Webster at the top of page 12.

Fame is a vapor,
popularity an accident,
riches take wings.
Only one thing endures,
and that is character.
　　　　　—Horace Greeley

Abe Buys a Barrel

Mary Nygaard Peterson

This play about Abraham Lincoln is based on facts about his life, but the details and the dialogue are invented by the author. How many facts about Abe do you recognize in the play?

CHARACTERS

ABE LINCOLN, *young man,*
　　twenty-four years old
BILL BERRY, *his partner*
JACK KELSO, *his friend*
MENTOR GRAHAM, *the schoolteacher*
MRS. HORNBUCKLE, *a customer*
RUSSEL GODBEY, *a farmer*
JIM JENSEN, *a traveler*
HANNAH JENSEN, *his wife*
PETER,
　　　　　} *their children*
REBECCA,

TIME: *A summer morning in 1833.*
SETTING: *The Lincoln-Berry general store in New Salem, Ill.*
AT RISE: ABE LINCOLN *is lying on the counter reading a book. There is a period of silence, broken after an interval by the sound of someone rattling the door. It gradually occurs to ABE that someone is trying to get in. He turns the book face down on the counter, goes to the door and opens it.*

ABE: Come in, Mrs. Hornbuckle.

MRS. HORNBUCKLE *(Entering)*: Is the store open? I didn't really know whether you were here yet or not.

ABE: I'm here. I just hadn't gotten around to opening the door yet.

MRS. HORNBUCKLE: That's all right, Mr. Lincoln. I wouldn't want you to open it any earlier than usual just for me.

ABE: There's no one I'd rather open it for. What can I do for you this morning?

MRS. HORNBUCKLE: I'd like half a pound of tea. I didn't realize I was out of it, and I just don't enjoy my breakfast without it.

ABE: You shall have your tea, ma'am. *(He measures out tea, weighs it, puts it in paper packet, and hands it to MRS. HORNBUCKLE.)* Here you are. I hope you enjoy your breakfast.

MRS. HORNBUCKLE *(Taking tea)*: I will now, thanks to you. And here is your money. *(She digs deep into a worn, old-fashioned purse and hands him coin.)*

ABE: Thank you. Come in again, won't you?

MRS. HORNBUCKLE: Oh, I will, thank you. (ABE *escorts her to door, and she goes out. He returns to counter, picks up book again, and sits on counter, his legs dangling over the edge.)*

ABE *(Muses)*: "To thine own self be true. . . . Thou canst not then be false to any man." *(Pause)* "To thine own self be true"— Hm-m-m. *(Door opens and BILL enters wearily.)*

BILL *(Approaching counter)*: Howdy, Abe. How's business? *(He pushes his straw hat back on his head and looks around.)*

ABE: Same as usual, Bill. Not rushing. All I've sold this morning is a half pound of tea. (ABE *gets down from counter and starts to straighten merchandise. He takes weight off scale and as he looks at it, stops suddenly, obviously upset.*) Jumping crickety!

BILL: What's the matter, Abe?

ABE: I charged Mrs. Hornbuckle for half a pound of tea and used only a four-ounce weight on the scale!

BILL: Oh, well, never mind—the old girl can afford it. And we need the money a lot worse'n she does.

ABE: Maybe so, but she's still got another fourth of a pound of tea coming to her. I'll measure it out right now before I forget. (*He measures out a small packet of tea, writes her name on it, and leaves it on the counter.*)

BILL: Suit yourself, Abe. (*He shrugs.*) But I just don't see how we're goin' to stay in business the way things are goin'. Have you any money, Abe?

ABE (*Jingling a few coins in his jeans*): Not more'n a few cents left from what Coleman Smoot paid me for pitchin' hay for him last week. But Russ Godbey promised to come in today to pay me for the work I did at his place. I have plenty of places to spend it, too. Need new pants, for one thing. I remember I had to split four hundred rails for each yard of cloth in these jeans. Nancy Miller sewed them up for me. They sure have been good pants, but you can't expect anythin' to last forever.

BILL (*He goes to the door, right, and looks out.*): I'll bet there are a hundred people in New Salem, an' not a soul stirring. Where do they keep themselves? (*He turns back into the room in disgust.*) No business. I might just as well have stayed in bed. (*He sits on a chair, tilts it back against the wall, then pulls his hat* *down over his eyes.)* Call me if you need me, Abe. I'm bone tired. *(It is quiet in the room.* ABE *picks up his book and paces up and down reading it.* JACK KELSO *enters, right, carrying a fishing pole.)*

JACK: Is this the firm of Lincoln and Berry—dealers in general merchandise?

ABE *(Laughing):* Depends on who's askin'. If it's bill collectors, we just moved out of town—forwardin' address unknown. *(Then, changing his tone.)* What's on your mind, Jack?

JACK: Fishin'. It's a perfect morning for fishin'. How about comin' with me? I'll fish an' you can read—an' if the fish won't bite, we can talk.

ABE *(Doubtfully):* I don't know, Jack. Maybe I'd better not—someone might want to buy something. We could sure use a few customers. Besides, Bill's sleepin' an' I kinda hate to wake him up just to tell him I'm goin' fishin'.

JACK: I'm in no hurry—the fish can wait. *(He takes a book out of his pocket, pushes a chair up against a wall, and settles himself down to read.* ABE *sits with his book.* RUSSEL GODBEY *enters.)*

GODBEY: Hello, Abe. I brought in your pay, just like I said I would.

ABE: That's good. My bank account's gettin' kinda low— an' my pants are gettin' kinda high—as you can see.

GODBEY *(Shifts about uncomfortably):* Well, now, Abe, I kinda hoped you wouldn't need to be paid in cash.

ABE *(Crestfallen):* Why, ah—are things runnin' kinda low for you, too, Russ?

GODBEY: Just seems like I can't make both ends meet, Abe—had to get me a new plow if I wanted to stay in farmin'. Then the Missus said she had to get clothes for the young'uns—seems they had nothin' to wear.

ABE: In that case, why don't we just forget the whole thing? I know it takes a heap of money where there's a family of young'uns to support.

GODBEY: Oh, I don't want to forget it, Abe. I always aim to pay my debts, somehow. I wondered if you might have any use for these two buckskins? *(Shows him skins)* They're real nice skins.

ABE *(Feeling skins)*: Why, yes, Russ—I'd be glad to take the skins for pay. They *are* real nice skins.

GODBEY: Thanks, Abe, for bein' so accommodatin'. If there's ever anythin' we can do for you, all you have to do is name it.

ABE: I'll sure do that, Russ. (GODBEY *exits, right.* ABE *folds the skins up and puts them away.)*

JACK: I see you're gettin' rich fast, Abe—just like me.

ABE: I wouldn't worry about gettin' rich, if I could just break even. Well, I guess there go my new pants. *(He shrugs and grins. JENSEN enters right. He stands uncertainly near the door until ABE looks up and sees him.)* Howdy, stranger. I didn't see you standin' there. Something I can do for you?

JENSEN *(Wringing his hands nervously):* Well, ah—I've got a barrel out in my wagon. I wondered if you might be interested in buyin' it?

ABE: What's in the barrel?

JENSEN *(Shifting his feet uneasily):* Oh—nothin', I guess— just junk. We're movin' West, an' I'd like to get the thing out of the way.

ABE: Well, I don't rightly need a barrel, but I can look at it, I guess. (ABE *and* JENSEN *exit.* BILL *shifts his position but continues sleeping.* JACK *reads.* MENTOR GRAHAM *enters and looks around.)*

MENTOR: Abe here?

JACK: Out buyin' a barrel.

MENTOR: A barrel of what? (JACK *shrugs.* ABE *enters with* MRS. JENSEN *and her two children.)*

ABE: Now you just sit here an' make yourself comfortable, Mrs. Jensen. *(He takes a chair and places it near the counter for her.)* An' you two young'uns sit here. *(He picks up children and sets them on counter.)* We'll see that you get some crackers an' milk to take away that hungry feelin'.

JACK: I'll get it for 'em, Abe. Where do you keep the milk?

ABE: There's a bucket of milk in the back room. Bowling Green brought it over—his wife told him I was gettin' too skinny, an' she wanted to fatten me up a little. *(He laughs and starts to leave, then notices that* MENTOR *has come in.* JACK *exits.)* Be with you in a minute, Mentor. *(He waves and exits, right. JACK comes in from the storeroom, left, with three tin cups on the lid of a box.)*

JACK: Here you are, kids. Do you like milk? *(He offers it to them and they accept it eagerly, but shyly, and nod their heads. MRS. JENSEN takes a cup, also.)*

MRS. JENSEN: Thankee, kindly. It's long since we ate, an' I'm sure I don't know where our next meal's comin' from. Peter, Rebecca—where's your manners? Did you say thanks for the milk?

JACK: That's all right. Let them enjoy themselves. *(He reaches into large bin, takes out two handfuls of crackers and puts them on box lid, which he holds out to children.)*

PETER and **REBECCA** *(Helping themselves)*: Thankee. Thankee.

MRS. JENSEN *(Helping herself)*: Thankee, Mister.

JACK: Eat all you want—all you can hold. Abe wants you to. *(He puts the lid between the children and returns to his chair.)*

MENTOR *(Looking inside the covers of the book on the counter)*: Looks like Abe borrowed this from you, Jack.

JACK: Yep. He reads everything he can get his hands on— makes no difference what it is.

MENTOR: I know. He'll *get* somewhere, someday—with that brain of his.

JACK: Yep. The place he'd like to get most right now is out of debt. He sure worries about those debts of his. (ABE *enters, rolling a barrel in on its rim.)*

ABE *(Speaking over his shoulder)*: This'll come in real handy, one of these days. (MR. JENSEN *follows* ABE, *but says nothing.* ABE *digs into his pocket.)* Here's four bits. I know it's not much, but it's all I can pay.

MR. JENSEN: Thankee, Mister. That's about all it's worth,

I reckon. *(Then, to his wife)* You ready to start, Hannah? (MRS. JENSEN *rises and helps the children down.)*

MRS. JENSEN: Come on, Peter, Rebecca. Your Pappy's ready to start.

ABE: Wait a minute. *(He reaches into candy jar and gives each of the children a piece of candy.)* Here's a drop for each of you. Suck on that an' the way won't seem so long.

MRS. JENSEN *(Almost tearfully):* Thankee kindly, Sir. We all feel much better, now. *(Then, to the children)* What do you say to the man—Peter, Rebecca?

PETER and **REBECCA** *(Shyly):* Thankee, Sir.

ABE: That's all right. *(He escorts them to the door.)* Good luck to you out West! *(They exit, and* ABE *walks back to counter.)*

JACK: What a store! Seems to me you're givin' out more'n you're takin' in.

ABE: Oh, I dunno. The barrel *might* come in handy someday. You never can tell. Why, I might even have to wear it if I don't earn enough money for some new clothes soon.

JACK *(Jeering):* Now, Abe, you won't need clothes for a long time. Didn't Godbey just pay you a couple of perfectly good buckskins?

ABE *(Looks thoughtful for a moment, and then suddenly):* You're dead right, Jack. I know just what I can do with those buckskins—I can take them over to Jack Armstrong's and have his wife fix my pants with them—you know, sew them on the bottom and the insides of the legs! They'll wear like iron. Maybe I'll never need to buy another pair of pants.

JACK: Well, now that you have that settled, why don't we set a match to this ol' barrel an' go fishin'?

MENTOR *(He peers into it.):* Wonder what all that junk is. It's almost full. *(He gingerly reaches inside barrel.)*

ABE: You've got me curious now. *(Reaches into barrel.)* I don't imagine it's anything very valuable. When poor folks throw away somethin', it's generally not worth much. Well, what do you know? *(He begins tugging on something and pulls out an old bonnet.)* Anyone need a new bonnet? *(He plops it on JACK'S head.)* Makes you look real handsome, Jack.

JACK *(Flinging the hat away from him):* Hey! Have a heart.

ABE *(Continuing to dig):* New shoes, anyone? *(He hauls out a pair of high-heeled, pointed ladies' shoes, tied together.)* Looks like they'd about fit you, Mentor. *(He dangles them enticingly in front of MENTOR but MENTOR refuses to touch them. ABE lets them fall to the floor. BILL stirs, yawns, and wakes up to find ABE lifting some garments out of the barrel.)*

BILL: What in the world have you there, Abe?

ABE: Just a barrel I bought from a hard-up stranger.

BILL *(Grumpily):* We're plenty hard-up ourselves, without you buyin' junk that other folks throw away.

ABE *(Comfortingly):* Don't worry, Bill, I paid for it out of my own pocket—a whole fifty cents.

BILL *(Pacified):* Well, that's different. Though I can't see how you have any extra money to spend. I know I don't. Russ Godbey must have been in to pay you.

ABE *(Absently):* He was. *(He continues to take things out of the barrel.)* Well, look what I found! *(He holds up a big book.)*

JACK: A book! Say, you should like that, Abe.

ABE: Yep. Maybe this *isn't* all junk. *(He reads the title from the back of the book.)* Blackstone's *Commentaries on English Law.* Hip, hip, hooray! *(He flings his arms jubilantly into the air and dances a few awkward hops.)*

JACK: Sounds like kinda dull readin' to me. Too bad it isn't Shakespeare.

ABE *(Decidedly):* No, sir-ee. This is the book fellows have to read before they can become lawyers. John Stuart over in Springfield was tellin' me. He said I could even read this by myself, an' then if I could pass the bar examinations, I could be a lawyer. *(He looks thoughtful.)* There should be—I wonder if—*(He reaches into barrel again.)* There should be more—yes, sir, here's another! *(He takes out another huge volume. He puts it on top of the first one, on the floor, and pulls out another.)* An' here's the third one, and the fourth. *(He examines the last one.)* Yes, sir, they're all here! *(He hugs them all and jumps about with them.)* Boy, oh, boy, oh, boy! This is my lucky day!

BILL *(Unbelieving):* You gonna *read* all those big books, Abe?

ABE: Not read 'em, Bill—*study* 'em. Why, these books must have cost almost a fortune. I could never own them, except by accident. An' to think we almost set a match to 'em!

JACK: You think you'll really be a lawyer someday, Abe?

ABE: Maybe. John Stuart said if I ever did pass those bar examinations, he'd be glad to take me into his law office with him, over in Springfield. *(Suddenly thoughtful, then, seeming to lose his confidence.)* Only one thing bothers me about bein' a lawyer, though.

JACK: What's that?

ABE: The way I talk. I know I don't talk right. A lawyer's got to know how to talk—he's got to make speeches to the court an' jury, an' they'd just laugh at me the way I talk now. I could never win a case.

BILL: What difference does it make how you talk—long as people understand what you're sayin'? You sound all right to me.

MENTOR: No, Abe's right. We all know how smart Abe is. He's going to amount to something someday—maybe even be a famous man. He ought to learn to talk right.

ABE: But what's a fellow to do when he has to earn a livin'? I can't take time out to go to school. Why, I don't reckon I've been to school a year all together in my life, so far.

BILL: I still say it doesn't matter. Look at President Andy Jackson—d'you s'pose he knows any more'n you do? I'll bet he doesn't know half as much—an' he got to be President. What more d'you want?

MENTOR *(Thoughtfully):* I was just thinking, Abe. Vanner has a grammar book over at his place—*Kirkham's Grammar.* I saw it over there, and I'm sure he'd let you borrow it. You could study it odd minutes here at the store, and I could help you at night if you needed any help.

ABE: You'd be willin' to do that?

MENTOR: Be glad to, Abe.

ABE: Then I'll sure go over to Vanner's an' borrow that book right now. *(He looks at* BILL.*)* You goin' to stay awake now, Bill?

BILL *(Grumpily):* Guess I can if I have to. No business anyhow.

ABE *(Stuffing letters into the band inside his hat.):* I might as well move the United States Post Office into my hat an' deliver these letters at the same time . . . *(Looks around and sees* MRS. HORNBUCKLE's *tea. He stuffs package into his pocket.)* an' take Mrs. Hornbuckle's tea to her. *(He heads for the door, looks back as he steps out, and calls.)* So long, I'll be seein' you.

JACK *(Howling):* Abe! Oh, Abe—aren't you goin' fishin' with me? *(When there is no answer, he shrugs in despair.)* That's Abe for you! Six miles out to Vanner's and six miles back—for a grammar!

MENTOR *(Smiling):* I guess he's gone off on a tack of his own, now.

BILL: An' when he does that, there's no turnin' him back or stoppin' him. You can bank on that. *(He goes behind the counter ready to wait on customers.)* He'll be a lawyer for sure, now.

MENTOR: And here's another thing you can bank on—when he *is* a lawyer, he'll be a mighty good one. Wait and see!

JACK *(Musing half to himself as the others watch him):* Abe will be a mighty good lawyer. And maybe he'll be even more than a lawyer. Why, maybe someday Abe will even get to go to Washington—as a Congressman

---

tack—*a mission*

or a Senator. Why, it wouldn't surprise me if Abe Lincoln even became President of the United States someday. President Abraham Lincoln! I'll bet Abe could do it. *(Curtain)*

THE END

Character Theme—Honesty & Generosity

Time to Think

1. What is the climax of the play—the point of most intense interest?
2. What is significant about the barrel? How does this relate to Abe's future?
3. Why did Abe buy the barrel?
4. How did Abe's friends know he would be a good lawyer?
5. What character qualities in Abe did the author show that later contributed to his success? Explain your answers by giving lines from the play that show these qualities.

LINCOLN

Nancy Byrd Turner

There was a boy of other days,
A quiet, awkward, earnest lad,
Who trudged long weary miles to get
A book on which his heart was set—
And then no candle had!

He was too poor to buy a lamp
But very wise in woodmen's ways.
He gathered seasoned bough and stem,
And crisping leaf, and kindled them
Into a ruddy blaze.

Then as he lay full length and read,
The firelight flickered on his face,
And etched his shadow on the gloom,
And made a picture in the room,
In that most humble place.

The hard years came, the hard years went,
But, gentle, brave, and strong of will,
He met them all. And when today
We see his pictured face, we say,
"There's light upon it still."

The Lone Eagle

Irving Crump

"I am Charles A. Lindbergh."
As if Paris did not know who he
was! Charles Lindbergh, the first
man to fly from New York to Paris, thus modestly introduced
himself on that memorable day of May 21, 1927. Paris was wild
with delight. The cables between France and America, and
between France and every other civilized country in the world,
were crowded with messages telling of the brave young man's
safety. Yet Lindbergh, ignorant of the fame into which he had
flown, and without knowing that millions of persons during the
preceding thirty-four hours had been praying for his safety, was
reaching for his wallet, to present his letters of introduction.

Young Lindbergh, crowd-shy and tired, had captured the
imagination of the globe. He was America's hero and the idol
of every nation in the world. He had accomplished a feat which
had brought to others suffering and death, and he had done it
alone.

"It wasn't any picnic." This was his first comment on the
perilous trip,—just that. He did not have time to say more at
that minute. He was seized by the crowds at the Paris airdrome
and carried about on the shoulders of the military men and
citizens, until with great difficulty he was rescued.

"Doesn't anyone here speak English?" he inquired. Yes, an
American newspaper correspondent did, and Lindbergh, conqueror of the Atlantic, grasping the arm of his new-found friend,
held closely to it until the American ambassador, Mr. Herrick,
had begun his safe conduct to the American Embassy.

---

airdrome—*airport*

"Lindbergh the Lucky," "The Flying Fool," "Slim"—these were but a few of the many nicknames by which Charles Lindbergh became known on account of his perilous flight. Now Lindbergh was not a snob. As a lover of jokes himself, he even liked nicknames, but he did resent having the newspapers call him "Lucky Lindbergh" and "The Flying Fool." He denied that luck had made him victor in his flight; for months he had earnestly prepared for the trip, having supervised even the construction of his plane to the last detail.

Charles Lindbergh was destined to be a farmer. His father had been a member of the House of Representatives from the Little Falls district of Minnesota; but his father was a farmer, too, and after his father's death, young Lindbergh endeavored to carry on the work. As he guided the plow his thoughts, however, were elsewhere. The youth's ambitions to become an airman would not stay down. He completed his course in the Little Falls High School and for a time was a student in the University of Wisconsin, where he entered a course in chemistry. Because he was at heart an engineer, his soul could not rest until he had helped to build an airplane and had learned to fly.

Too young to take part in World War I, Lindbergh determined to enter the Army Air Corps soon after the armistice. In his eighteenth year, he journeyed by motorcycle to Kelly Field, in San Antonio, Texas, and enrolled as a cadet for the air service. There he made swift progress, found out that he was naturally a flyer—that he possessed the "bird instinct"—and received his discharge a year later as First Lieutenant of the Army Reserve Corps. The training he received at Kelly Field gave Lindbergh the groundwork without which success in any calling is impossible.

After receiving his discharge from Kelly Field, he rode his motorcycle to Lambert Field, St. Louis, and obtained employment with an aircraft company. The same year he received a

armistice—*a peace agreement that brings an end to fighting*

commission as Captain in the Missouri National Guard, and was appointed Flight Commander of the Flying Corps of the State. Later, in the Air Mail Service, he learned what a plane could do, and what he himself could force the plane to accomplish. The confidence which he gained in himself made him a capable flyer.

While carrying the mails between St. Louis and Chicago, night after night, Captain Lindbergh dreamed of conquering the Atlantic. He had read of Commander Byrd, René Fonck, and Nungesser, and wished to conquer the air as they had done. He had flown in every condition known to man except over the ocean; and how many of the aces of the world knew anything of over-the-ocean flying? Without belittling the accomplishments of others, his supreme confidence told him that he was competent. Flying was his own profession.

Night after night, in clear weather and fog, through rain or snow, for a whole year before his dream became a reality, Lindbergh pondered over the Atlantic flight. How could he do it? He knew it would require money to make the effort. He knew that he would need a specially built plane, but he knew that if he conquered the Atlantic he would have the $25,000 prize to pay back the debts he had made in the enterprise.

He did not speak of his ambitions to many, but went upon his way, quietly trying to interest a few other men. While riding above the storms during the dark nights with the mails, he thought out the best way to accomplish his aims. He determined to go to the officers of the Robertson Aircraft Company, from whom he had obtained his first employment at Lambert Field, and by whom he had been given his position as Air Mail flyer. A former army man, Major William B. Robertson, president of the firm, was convinced by Lindbergh's belief that he could make the flight; Robertson was so confident of his employee's ability that he told several wealthy residents of St. Louis that it was their

---

competent—*capable*

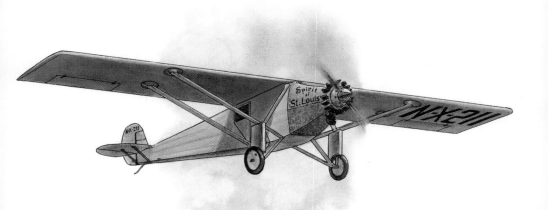

duty to provide Captain Lindbergh with the plane required for his trip; he presented Lindbergh's claims so well that he won his point.

In fact, after these men of St. Louis felt that Lindbergh could cross the Atlantic, the only conditions stated were that he should be his own manager, and that no second person should be brought in to confuse matters. This was a compliment to his own rare judgment. From boyhood, he had been the "Lone Eagle." Everything that he had done in his life had been done alone; he had maintained his confidence in this ability by flying alone with the mail.

A youth by the name of Donald Hall, who came from Brooklyn, designed a plane for him; Lindbergh actively supervised every step of the construction. He and Hall planned just the craft that Lindbergh wanted. In all particulars it was like the plane regularly made by the Ryan Company, except that Lindbergh and Hall added ten feet to the wingspread and placed the fuel tank under the wing. They placed the cockpit behind, making it necessary for the pilot to use periscopes to see ahead of him.

Experts said the *Spirit of St. Louis* was the oddest looking aircraft, from the cockpit, anyway, that they had ever seen. When Lindbergh tested the plane and found that it met every requirement, he sent in his entry for the $25,000 Orteig prize.

Accustomed to making his own decisions, he was not greatly interested in what others thought about his intended flight.

On May 9, 1927, he mounted his machine, which he had named the *Spirit of St. Louis,* and set off from San Diego, California, where the plane was made, to New York. After fourteen hours and five minutes in the air, he made his first stop at St. Louis to let his backers see the ship.

Until that time no one outside of the Army and the Postal Service knew much about Lindbergh. As a matter of fact, he was not taken very seriously. Everyone asked how such an obscure person could attempt to compete with notables like Byrd, Chamberlin, Fonck, or with such men as Nungesser and Coli.

Yet aviators and the public in general began to stir themselves when they learned about Lindbergh's flight from San Diego to St. Louis in record time, and this by a mere mail pilot who knew little about navigation. They marveled that he had reached St. Louis and had been only fifteen miles out of the true course.

On this flight his compass had been so faulty that he had not been able to place any faith in it. He had carried no instrument to indicate the drift of his machine, another important factor in both ships of the sea and ships of the air. Indeed, this wonderful accomplishment under difficulties made the youthful flyer respected by experienced flyers. While they did not believe he could cross the ocean as a "lone eagle," they conceded that he was a natural flyer. He rested overnight at St. Louis after his feat, and the next day, May 11, 1927, he sped away for Curtiss Field, New York, where he arrived after having been in the air but seven hours and eleven minutes.

Then New York and all of the contenders for the Orteig prize could see him, and seeing, realize that this man they had heard about did actually exist. This man who could fly by day or

---

obscure—*unknown*   conceded—*admitted*

night, in all sorts of weather even with faulty compasses, could instinctively reach his goal.

When Friday, May 20, 1927, arrived, Lindbergh was ready to go; rain and chill weather did not change his determination; neither did the fact that he had had no sleep during the previous night. He clambered into the blind cockpit of his plane, where all of his seeing must be done by means of instruments, sat down in the little wicker seat, poked his head out and said, "So long."

That was Lindbergh, the confident. He acted as if he were starting to cross a lake in a motorboat, or going for a ride into the country. No cheering Godspeeds or yells for him; just "So long."

The Lone Eagle and the *Spirit of St. Louis* were on their way to France.

From that moment until he landed at the Paris airdrome, Lindbergh had the fervent prayers of all the world. Some said that the hum of his motor would hypnotize him, would lull him to sleep before he ever reached his goal. Others were certain that a single-motored plane would never have the endurance to make the flight of two thousand miles. Still others sincerely believed that a man who carried no sextant could never find his way from New York to Paris alone. Then, too, the weather experts served to spread gloom. They expected storms and believed that the pilot would not be able to weather them.

Lindbergh had barely left Newfoundland when a terrific sleet storm broke. The pilot was beset on all sides by the elements. Howling, wind-driven particles of ice were above him and below him. They meant peril, and, for all he knew, death, for nothing is more dangerous to aircraft than sleet. This is an element that is not shed readily, like rain; it sticks fast wherever it lands. The weight of the sleet upon the wings of a plane causes them to curl downward, thus taking the craft out of the aviator's control. The weight of the sleet on Lindbergh's plane was tremendous. He later confessed that he really had a strong desire at this point to turn back. But he decided that to turn back would not necessarily mean safety because he would still be in the storm; he reasoned that perhaps to go on would be just as safe. He continued on his way.

First, he climbed to an altitude of more than ten thousand feet, but still he could not rise above the storm. Then he almost skimmed the surface of the water, but still could find no escape from the peril. As night began to fall he approached fields of icebergs, which he could see plainly. Their nearness made him rise to a good height again, because he did not wish to end his flight by a collision. He climbed to about twelve thousand feet, and, to his relief, found that he had risen above the sleet. If he had been another hour in the storm, he might never have been heard from again.

The cold at twelve thousand feet is intense, but Captain Lindbergh was well equipped with clothing, and while the frost nipped at him, he did not mind it greatly. His long practice in flying the United States mail under similar conditions stood him in good stead.

His plane, not equipped with radio, could not signal to the ships at sea. People could do nothing but wait for the hour when he should be sighted. If he was seen, all would be well; if not, the world would have to wait for tidings or remain forever baffled by the same sort of mystery that enshrouded the French flyers who had been lost a few days before. Every ship at sea was under orders to watch for the plane, but as Lindbergh was flying out of the regular transatlantic lane, not much news was expected from that source.

---

enshrouded—*surrounded*

In the early afternoon of the next day, May 21, a fleet of fishing boats far off the Irish coast received a thrill when a plane came down from the skies with a roar, flew so close to some of them that they feared disaster, and then flew away again with a deafening roar. If they only had known, the aviator in the plane was Lindbergh, who had yelled to them from his cockpit an inquiry as to the direction in which Ireland lay. He had forgotten, in his earnestness, that they would not hear his voice above the roar of the engine, and that if they could, he would not hear their response.

Nevertheless, Captain Lindbergh was on the correct route and flying in the true direction. About one hour later he was over Ireland. He was so joyous at seeing land again that he flew low to drink in all of the scenery his limited field of vision would permit. He knew where he was—he had the map of Ireland spread out before him—and from that point forward he had no need to worry about direction. The landmarks indicated in his charts were appearing beneath him regularly, and he had daylight for the rest of his trip. He had fought and won his battle in the dark over the broad Atlantic. Now the daylight was to be his until almost the end of his historic flight.

Over Ireland and England he flew rather low in order that he might be sighted, crossed the English Channel, and arrived over French territory for the first time near Cherbourg. Then he gave himself a great thrill by finding the Seine River, recognizing it, and following it all the way to Paris.

When he was about sixty miles away from the great city, he saw rockets and other signal lights, and realized that they were meant for him. Finally, he found the Eiffel Tower, near Paris, and from that point looked around for a landing field.

He became confused, because in France both the flood lights and the beacon lights at the flying field are lighted,

---

Cherbourg (shĕr·boorg´)

whereas in America, when a pilot is expected to land, the beacons are dimmed and only the flood lights show where the landing is to be made. Therefore, instead of descending, he sped away and encircled Paris, looking for another landing place. His search was unsuccessful, and he concluded that the first field he had seen was his destination.

Two minutes later Lindbergh and the *Spirit of St. Louis* had descended into fame.

Character Theme—Courage & Initiative

Time to Think

1. Is the title, "The Lone Eagle" appropriate for this selection? Explain your answer.
2. Why did Lindbergh resent nicknames that credited his success to "luck"?
3. The author says "the training he received at Kelly Field gave Lindbergh the groundwork without which success in any calling is impossible." Explain how success depends on groundwork.
4. Do you think it was to Lindbergh's advantage to know exactly how his plane was constructed? Why?
5. What does Lindbergh's consideration about turning back during the sleet storm reveal about him?
6. How did Lindbergh react to public acclaim?

America's Poet

Ellen Wilson

"Going his own way" took Robert Frost through the authorship of many books of poetry, through familiar joys and sorrows, through prizes and public honors in many places. Before he died in 1963, his stride had taken him to all parts of our country. It had taken him to faraway countries, including Israel, Greece, and Russia.

Wherever Frost went, his poetry opened doors for him. He even lost his fear of appearing on public platforms. This happened when he simply *said* his poems instead of trying to lecture and make speeches.

People everywhere were delighted to listen. Often they asked him to say "Birches," a poem that had been swinging in his mind ever since he was a boy. Another favorite was "Stopping by Woods on a Snowy Evening." This one ended with the lines,

> "But I have promises to keep,
> And miles to go before I sleep,
> And miles to go before I sleep."

Amherst and many other colleges claimed Robert Frost as teacher. Universities all over the country and abroad awarded him honorary degrees because of his poetry. With each degree came a bright-colored hood of shining silk or satin or soft velvet.

"All together they will make a fine patchwork quilt," he said. "Bright as a rainbow and warm as a freestone on a cold winter night."

The climax came when Frost was invited to say a poem at the inauguration of John F. Kennedy in Washington, D.C., January 20, 1961. On Inauguration Day, the air was bitterly cold, but the sun was dazzling on the snow and ice. It shone bright on tens of thousands of excited people who had gathered for the occasion. They lined the avenues and Capitol Plaza, bundled up in mufflers, furs, coats, and blankets.

All eyes were on the flag-bedecked platform where the nation's youngest President and the country's oldest poet were sitting. John F. Kennedy himself had invited Frost to attend and take part in the inauguration.

Neither President nor poet seemed to mind the freezing weather in Washington. Each of them had known deeper snows and colder days than this in New England.

"Besides," Frost thought as he waited on the platform, "today is a day to warm the cockles of the heart. Poets and statesmen are getting together at last."

Frost remembered how disappointed he had been seventy-five years before, when he was a boy of eleven and couldn't come to the inauguration of President Cleveland. Now here he was eighty-six years old, the first poet ever asked to take part in an inauguration.

Frost rose with all the others at the stirring sound of "The Star-Spangled Banner." As Marian Anderson sang this song, her rich voice rolled out on the clear, cold air.

---

freestone—*a stone that was heated and used as a bed-warmer on cold nights*

climax—*the most important part or event*

Cardinal Cushing of Boston gave a long and earnest prayer. The new Vice-President, Lyndon B. Johnson of Texas, took the oath of office. The new President would be sworn in later.

Soon it would be Frost's turn on the program. At Kennedy's request he would say his most patriotic poem, "The Gift Outright." This was an old poem, which he knew by heart. No need to be nervous over that!

But the poet was planning a surprise. Yesterday and until the last minute that very morning he had worked on a brand-new poem in honor of the President. He planned to read this poem because he hadn't really learned it yet. Nervously he felt in his pocket for the papers on which the poem was written to make sure they were there.

Suddenly Frost was introduced to the vast audience. He stood at the speaker's stand, bulky in his heavy gray overcoat, his scarf tucked around his throat, his white hair blowing in the winter wind.

He began to read his surprise poem, but something went wrong. The stiff wind tore at his papers and the glare of the sun made the letters dance before his eyes. He couldn't even see the words. He stumbled over them. His voice faltered, his hands trembled.

From the front row President and Mrs. John F. Kennedy, President Dwight D. Eisenhower, and all the other persons present watched in anxious sympathy. Lyndon B. Johnson, the new Vice-President, jumped up to help. He held out his top hat to cut off the sun and cast a shadow on the poet's papers. Perhaps this would help the famous poet.

But no. No one could help except Frost himself. Thousands in the audience held their breath in sympathy. Would the poet have to give up and sit down in failure?

Suddenly Frost gave up trying to read the new poem. He put the papers in his pocket, aware that he had promises to keep. Squaring his shoulders, he lifted his head with renewed courage.

Then straight from the heart he said his old poem beginning, "The land was ours before we were the land's."

Now, full of spunk, Robert Frost stood sure and straight, braced against the wind and weather. His voice came clear and strong down through the very last line of "The Gift Outright," his poem about America: "Such as she was, such as she will become."

Millions of people, watching and listening in Washington and on television, felt a new surge of pride in their country. They felt pride, too, in this man of courage who spoke for them. Robert Frost was their poet, the poet of all America.

---

spunk—*brave spirit, eagerness*

Character Theme—Courage & Patriotism

Time to Think

1. At whose inauguration was Mr. Frost invited to speak?
2. What happened when Mr. Frost tried to read the new poem he had written for the President?
3. What is the poem "The Gift Outright" about?
4. Why do you think Robert Frost was called America's poet? What made his poetry so popular?

The Gift Outright

Robert Frost

The land was ours before we were the land's.
She was our land more than a hundred years
Before we were her people. She was ours
In Massachusetts, in Virginia,
But we were England's, still colonials,
Possessing what we still were unpossessed by,
Possessed by what we now no more possessed.
Something we were withholding made us weak
Until we found out that it was ourselves
We were withholding from our land of living,
And forthwith found salvation in surrender.
Such as we were we gave ourselves outright
(The deed of gift was many deeds of war)
To the land vaguely realizing westward,
But still unstoried, artless, unenhanced,
Such as she was, such as she would become.

MEET THE POET

Robert Frost is one of America's most widely read poets. He was born in 1874 in San Francisco but grew up in New England. It was in New England that Mr. Frost learned to appreciate and see beauty in commonplace things like patches of snow, birch trees, stone walls, and wild grapes. He put his love for these things into the words of many memorable poems.

As he continued to write his rich but simple poetry, his fame grew and he received many awards.

Robert Frost died on January 29, 1963, in Boston. If he had lived another few weeks, he would have been eighty-nine years old. Americans still read and love his poems because of the joy and understanding that they bring.

41

WILD GRAPES

Robert Frost

. . . . One day my brother led me to a glade
Where a white birch he knew of stood alone,
Wearing a thin head-dress of pointed leaves,
And heavy on her heavy hair behind,
5   Against her neck, an ornament of grapes.
Grapes, I knew grapes from having seen them last year.
One bunch of them, and there began to be
Bunches all round me growing in white birches,
The way they grew round Leif the Lucky's German;
10   Mostly as much beyond my lifted hands, though,
As the moon used to seem when I was younger,
And only freely to be had for climbing.
My brother did the climbing; and at first
Threw me down grapes to miss and scatter
15   And have to hunt for in sweet fern and hardhack;
Which gave him some time to himself to eat,
But not so much, perhaps, as a boy needed.
So then, to make me wholly self-supporting,
He climbed still higher and bent the tree to earth
20   And put it in my hands to pick my own grapes.
'Here, take a tree-top. I'll get down another.
Hold on with all your might when I let go.'
I said I had the tree. It wasn't true.
The opposite was true. The tree had me.
25   The minute it was left with me alone
It caught me up as if I were the fish
And it the fishpole. So I was translated
To loud cries from my brother of 'Let go!
Don't you know anything, you girl? Let go!'

Leif the Lucky—*Leif Ericson*
German—*Germany*

hardhack—*a plant covered in soft down,
having small purple flowers*

42

30   But I, with something of the baby grip
Acquired ancestrally in just such trees
When wilder mothers than our wildest now
Hung babies out on branches by the hands
To dry or wash or tan, I don't know which,
35   (You'll have to ask an evolutionist)—
I held on uncomplainingly for life.
My brother tried to make me laugh to help me.
'What are you doing up there in those grapes?
Don't be afraid. A few of them won't hurt you.
40   I mean, they won't pick you if you don't them.'
Much danger of my picking anything!
By that time I was pretty well reduced
To a philosophy of hang-and-let-hang.
'Now you know how it feels,' my brother said,
45   'To be a bunch of fox-grapes, as they call them,
That when it thinks it has escaped the fox
By growing where it shouldn't—on a birch,
Where a fox wouldn't think to look for it—
And if he looked and found it, couldn't reach it—
50   Just then come you and I to gather it.
Only you have the advantage of the grapes
In one way: you have one more stem to cling by,
And promise more resistance to the picker.'

One by one I lost off my hat and shoes,
55   And still I clung. I let my head fall back,
And shut my eyes against the sun, my ears
Against my brother's nonsense; 'Drop,' he said,
'I'll catch you in my arms. It isn't far.'
(Stated in lengths of him it might not be.)
60   'Drop or I'll shake the tree and shake you down.'
Grim silence on my part as I sank lower,
My small wrists stretching till they showed the banjo strings.
'Why, if she isn't serious about it!
Hold tight awhile till I think what to do.

---

banjo strings—*tendons resembling the strings on a banjo*

65 I'll bend the tree down and let you down by it.'
    I don't know much about the letting down;
    But once I felt ground with my stocking feet
    And the world came revolving back to me,
    I know I looked long at my curled-up fingers,
70 Before I straightened them and brushed the bark off.
    My brother said: 'Don't you weigh anything?
    Try to weigh something next time, so you won't
    Be run off with by birch trees into space.'

    It wasn't my not weighing anything
75 So much as my not knowing anything—
    My brother had been nearer right before.
    I had not taken the first step in knowledge;
    I had not learned to let go with the hands,
    As still I have not learned to with the heart,
80 And have no wish to with the heart—nor need,
    That I can see. The mind—is not the heart.
    I may yet live, as I know others live,
    To wish in vain to let go with the mind—
    Of cares, at night, to sleep; but nothing tells me
85 That I need learn to let go with the heart.

Time to Think

1. What happened to the girl when she grabbed the branch that
   her brother bent down to her?

2. This incident reminded the poet that we should let go of
   cares and worries. Things of the heart we should hang on to,
   however. What might those be?

Now

Charles R. Skinner

If you have hard work to do,
   Do it now.
Today the skies are clear and blue,
Tomorrow clouds may come in view,
Yesterday is not for you;
   Do it now.

If you have a song to sing,
   Sing it now.
Let the notes of gladness ring
Clear as song of bird in Spring,
Let every day some music bring;
   Sing it now.

If you have kind words to say,
   Say them now.
Tomorrow may not come your way,
Do a kindness while you may,
Loved ones will not always stay;
   Say them now.

If you have a smile to show,
   Show it now.
Make hearts happy, roses grow,
Let the friends around you know
The love you have before they go;
   Show it now.

Lou Gehrig's Epic of Courage

Paul Gallico

I remember writing years ago: "There is no greater inspiration to any American boy than Lou Gehrig. For if the awkward, inept and downright clumsy player that I knew in the beginning could through sheer drive and determination turn himself into the finest first-base-covering machine in all baseball, then nothing is impossible to any man or boy in this country."

The last chapter in the life of this baseball hero puts a big exclamation point after that statement. Gehrig was at the height of his career.

The Yankees won the American League pennant in 1936–7–8. They won three World Series championships in a row.

Yes, it was a wonderful, gleaming, glittering golden success. Lou Gehrig was in the thick of it, driving in the runs, winning new honors, breaking and setting new records.

In 1936, Lou was again named the most valuable player in the American League, exactly nine years after he had first achieved this honor.

And in the meantime, his consecutive games record was going on and on as though it would never stop. He celebrated his 1,500th game, his 1,800th, his 1,900th and his 2,000th.

The simple engaging personality of Lou Gehrig became welded into the National scene. Came the baseball season, came Gehrig. Came Gehrig, came home runs, triples, doubles, excitement and faultless play around First Base. And his record ran on. Day in day out he played, sick or well, never missing a game.

He played with colds. He played with fevers. He played so doubled over with backache that it was impossible for him to straighten up.

In 1934, the year he won the triple crown, he fractured a toe. He played on. He was knocked unconscious by a wild pitch, suffered a concussion that would hospitalize the average man for two weeks. He was at his position the next day and collected four hits.

When his hands were X-rayed, late in his career, they found seventeen assorted fractures that had healed by themselves. He had broken every finger of both hands and some twice, and *hadn't even mentioned* it to anyone.

And in the winter of 1939 Lou and Eleanor as usual, went ice skating together. Lou was a fine skater. But, strangely, he kept falling all the time.

The teams went south for the 1939 training season and the sports writers went along with them. And the boys with one voice began sending back stories that must have saddened them to write. They asked . . . "What is the matter with Gehrig?"

And having asked, they answered it. They wrote that Gehrig was through. They hated to do so, but they owed a loyalty to their papers and to the people who read the papers. An honest reporter writes what he sees.

Sadly they wrote that Lou was going the way of all athletes. The old Iron Horse was running down.

But the players on the Yankee ball club were saying something else. One of the things they knew was that a ball player slows up only gradually. His legs go, imperceptibly at first, then noticeably as he no longer covers the ground in the field that he used to cover. But he doesn't come apart all at one time, and in chunks.

There are grim tales of things that happened in the locker room. One is of Gehrig dressing, leaning over to lace his spikes and falling forward to the floor to lie there momentarily helpless. And it tells further of tough men with the fine instincts to look away and not to hurt his already tortured soul the more by going to him or offering to help. Quickly they left the locker room leaving him to struggle to his feet alone with no eyes to see his weakness. They knew that it wasn't age that was bothering Gehrig, but that he was sick.

If you ask me what are some of the elements that go to make up a hero, I would say, among other things, the capacity for quiet, uncomplaining suffering, the ability to take it and never to let on, never to let the world suspect that you are taking it.

This was Lou Gehrig. Not even his wife knew wholly, though she must have suspected, how terribly Gehrig suffered during those days when his speed and skill were deserting him, when he found, to his bewilderment, that he could not bat, he could not run, and he could not field.

The strain and terror of it lined his face in a few short months and brought grey to his hair. But it could not force a complaint to his lips.

When it became apparent that there was something wrong with him, Lou drove himself still further, still harder, to punish his flagging muscles and sick body relentlessly.

He was certain that it was work he needed that fatal spring training session of 1939. It never occurred to him that something entirely different might be the matter with him or to blame for his apparent lack of physical condition, something quite outside his own powers to control.

His performance during the early part of 1939 was pitiful. On Sunday, April 30, 1939, the Yankees played the Senators in Washington. Lou Gehrig came to bat four times with runners on base. He failed to get a hit, or even meet the ball, and the Yankees lost.

Monday was an off day. Gehrig did a lot of thinking. He had the toughest decision of his life to make.

Tuesday, May 2nd, the team met in Detroit to open a series against the Tigers. Joe McCarthy, the Yankee manager, flew in from Buffalo. Lou met him in the dugout and said the fateful words:

"Joe, I always said that when I felt I couldn't help the team any more I would take myself out of the line-up. I guess that time has come."

McCarthy said: "When do you want to quit, Lou?"

Gehrig looked at him steadily and said, "Now."

His consecutive-games streak ended at 2,130 games.

Lou, at the urging of Eleanor, went up to the Mayo Clinic at Rochester, Minnesota, for a check-up.

The New York Yankees released the report of the Doctors at the Clinic. It was a form of Infantile Paralysis, and the mystery of the too sudden decline of Louis Henry Gehrig was solved.

Before Gehrig came home from the Mayo Clinic, Eleanor went to their family physician, gave him the name of the disease and asked to be told the truth about it. He told her that the disease was incurable and that her husband could not live more than two years.

Eleanor made a telephone call to the Mayo Clinic. She begged . . . "Please promise me that you won't tell my husband. Don't ever let him know. I don't want him to find out."

They promised.

Infantile Paralysis—*polio, a disease that causes the victim to become paralyzed*

Lou came home full of smiles and jokes, and the girl who met him was smiling and laughing too, though neither noticed that in the laughter of the other there was something a little feverish. They were too busy to notice. Too busy with their magnificent and gallant deception of one another. Eleanor fought a constant battle to keep the truth from Lou.

As to what Lou knew—he never told anybody.

On July 4th, 1939, there took place the most tragic and touching scene ever enacted on a baseball diamond.

Gehrig Day was a gesture of love and appreciation, a spontaneous reaching out to a man who had been good and kind and decent, to thank him for having been so.

Sixty-one thousand, eight hundred and eight were in the stands. It was what was known as a Great Day.

To Lou Gehrig, it was goodbye to everything that he had known and loved.

In the stands was all that he held dear, his family, mother and father seated in a box, unaware of his doom, his wife seated in another. Lifelong friends were in the boxes, cheering and applauding. And as Lou looked out over them gathered there in his honor, he knew he was seeing them thus for the last time.

The speeches were ended at last, the gifts given, and the stadium rocked as wave after wave of cheers rolled down from the stands and broke over him. For a little while as he stood at the microphones of the sound cameras and broadcasting companies, it seemed as though they might engulf him. He stood with his head bowed to the tumult—the tumult within and without, and pressed a handkerchief to his eyes to hold back the tears.

Everyone waited for what he would say. With a curled finger he dashed the tears that would not stay back from his eyes, lifted his head and spoke his epitaph. . . .

"For the past two weeks you have been reading about a bad break I got. Yet today, I consider myself the luckiest man on the face of the earth. . . ."

50

Although the tale of Lou Gehrig—American Hero, really ended above, he lived for quite a while longer, and perhaps the simple story of how he lived what time was left to him and what he did, is the most heroic deed of all, the bravest, most gallant and most self-sacrificing.

He chose to spend his last days, not in one final feverish attempt to suck from life in two years all that he might have had in forty, but in work and service.

Mayor LaGuardia appointed him a City Parole Commissioner. And so for the next months, as long as he was able to walk even with the assistance of others, Gehrig went daily to his office and did his work. He listened to cases, he studied them, he brought to it his thoroughness and his innate kindness and understanding.

He sat at his desk, even when no longer able to move his arms. He listened to thief, vagabond, and narcotic addict. When there was help to be given, he gave it unstintingly of what strength there was left to him. He would not give in. He would not give up. He did not give up.

On June 2, 1941, Lou Gehrig died in the arms of his wife in their home in Riverdale, New York.

Character Theme—Courage & Perseverance

Time to Think

1. Some athletes are very famous, but they are not great men. Was Lou Gehrig a great man?
2. Explain "the heroism of the laugh that covers pain."

FOOTPRINTS

Henry W. Longfellow

Lives of great men all remind us
　We can make our lives *sublime,*
And, departing, leave behind us
　Footprints on the sands of time—

Just as the footprints of brave pathfind-
ers have led their followers to success
and safety, so also have the wise words
of great men.　Memorials have been
built to honor many of these great men,
but the sincerest honor is paid by those
who strive to follow their examples.

sublime—*of great worth*

My Creed

*Theodore
Roosevelt*

I believe in honesty, sincerity, and the
　square deal; in making up one's mind
　what to do—and doing it.
I believe in fearing God and taking
　one's own part.
I believe in hitting the line hard when
　you are right.
I believe in speaking softly and carrying
　a big stick.
I believe in hard work and honest sport.
I believe in a sane mind in a sane body.
I believe we have room for but one
　soul loyalty, and that is loyalty to the
　American people.

Rules of Conduct

Author Unknown

When George Washington was about twelve years old, his brother had him copy the following rules into his notebook. George Washington tried to live by these rules throughout his life.

---

1. Every action in company ought to be with some sign of respect to those present.
2. Show not yourself glad at the misfortune of another, though he were your enemy.
3. When a man does all he can, though it succeeds not well, blame not him that did it.
4. Wherein you reprove another, be unblamable yourself; for example is more powerful than precepts.
5. Be not hasty to believe flying reports to the disparagement of any.
6. Associate yourself with men of good quality, if you esteem your own reputation, for it is better to be alone than in bad company.
7. Be not curious to know the affairs of others, neither approach to those that speak in private.
8. Undertake not what you cannot perform, but be careful to keep your promise.
9. Speak not evil of the absent, for it is unjust.
10. When you speak of God or His attributes, let it be seriously in reverence. Honor and obey your natural parents, although they be poor.
11. Let your recreations be manful, not sinful.
12. Labor to keep alive in your breast that little spark of celestial fire, called conscience.

---

reprove—*to point out wrong actions*
precepts—*rules or principles*
disparagement—*a loss of respect*

FROM
SECOND INAUGURAL ADDRESS

Abraham Lincoln

Abraham Lincoln's own words in this Second Inaugural Address show his compassion toward the South and his hopes for peace. This speech was delivered one month before the Civil War ended.

With malice toward none; with charity for all; with firmness in the right, as God gives us to see the right, let us strive on to finish the work we are in; to bind up the nation's wounds; to care for him who shall have borne the battle, and for his widow and his orphan—to do all which may achieve and cherish a just and lasting peace among ourselves and with all nations.

FROM A
SPEECH AT CONSTITUTIONAL CONVENTION

Benjamin Franklin

The longer I live, the more convincing proofs I see of this truth, that God governs in the affairs of man; and if a sparrow cannot fall to the ground without His notice, is it probable that an empire can rise without His aid?

FROM THE
DECLARATION OF INDEPENDENCE
Thomas Jefferson

We hold these truths to be self-evident, that all men are created equal; that they are endowed by their Creator with certain unalienable rights; that among these are life, liberty, and the pursuit of happiness.

unalienable—*that which cannot be taken away*

LIBERTY SPEECH
Patrick Henry

Is life so dear, or peace so sweet, as to be purchased at the price of chains and slavery? Forbid it, Almighty God! I know not what course others may take; but as for me, give me liberty, or give me death.

Time to Think

1. Why is it important that succeeding generations know about Washington, Lincoln, Jefferson, Franklin, and others?
2. Aren't they old-fashioned?

Colleen La Fon

The noise of children playing in the streets in Garfield Park, a dilapidated neighborhood in Chicago, drifted through the open window of the "homemade" classroom in the home of Mr. and Mrs. Clarence Collins.

"Those kids out there can learn, and I'm going to help them learn!" Marva Collins declared to her husband, who stood behind her. Mr. Collins's skilled hands had labored long to transform two back bedrooms into an organized classroom.

"We have worked so hard," continued Mrs. Collins; "I'll make it work!"

After teaching for twelve years in the Chicago public school system, Marva Collins's heart longed to help the children whom the other teachers considered hopeless. She knew that with love and consistent discipline and the right teaching methods these children could learn if she could instill within them pride and a desire to excel and to overcome the bad influences many of them faced in their neighborhoods.

Marva Collins had begun dreaming of opening a school of her own, and now, in 1977, she could see her dream coming true. Despite the piles of bills, the derision of other educators, the lack of supplies, and an enrollment of only five students, Mrs. Collins would be opening her school the next day.

Mr. Collins put his hand on her shoulder and squeezed it gently. "If you say it is going to work, then we will make it work, because you are the best teacher in the world."

---

derision—*ridicule*

56

Marva walked over to the chalkboard and wrote, "Welcome to Westside Preparatory School. Welcome to Success!" Clarence nodded his head in agreement as Marva vowed, "In this school we will be proud of who we are, and we will never say 'can't.' "

At eight o'clock the next morning, Mrs. Collins faced her class, which consisted of five black children, ages six to twelve. One of the students was her daughter, Cindy. The other four children had been called "learning impaired," "unteachable," or "dumb" by their former teachers in other schools. It was certainly true that none of them looked eager, capable, or even interested in learning.

Undaunted, Marva Collins began to enthusiastically explain success to these dull-eyed students who had never achieved success in anything they had ever done.

"No boredom, no baby work, and no more 'See Spot run' books! You get down the road of success only by hard work—memorizing a poem a week, writing a theme every day, and working with math and geography and spelling."

Mrs. Collins stood back to watch her students' reactions to this challenge. Hostility covered Martin's face. He was eleven and street-wise, and he had been expelled from every school he had ever gone to.

"I ain't doing none of that stuff," he spit out defiantly.

Marva moved within inches of Martin and knelt to face him on eye level. Her voice was low and quivering with emotion.

"*Am* not; I *am not* going to do *any* of that stuff," she corrected. "And if you do not learn, the only things in your future are welfare and poverty. Welfare is only another word for slavery. It keeps you down. Children on welfare do not live in big houses and go to Disney World for vacations. If you do not learn, you cannot work. There are no 'free rides,' and you have to work to get a decent life. In America you have the freedom to choose whether to learn or not to learn, but you do not have the freedom to keep others from learning; so stop interrupting, and let's get to work!"

With that, Mrs. Collins began teaching, totally in charge of her classroom. She never stayed in one place long. Writing a word on the chalkboard, kneeling in front of a student to encourage his efforts, hugging a student for his good answer—she never stopped captivating her students' interest or demanding their best work.

The first thing that she taught the students was the key to reading—phonics. They learned the sounds the letters represent instead of memorizing how each word looked when written. Within a few short months, Martin and the other pupils could read every word they could say.

Marva used reading to encourage the students' curiosity and ambition. They read the works of Shakespeare, Aesop, Chaucer—even Socrates. Whether in history class, science class, or language class, Mrs. Collins demanded that every student do his best.

"I don't want to hear any jive talk in this class. You must not just think of yourselves as ghetto children. You must strive to become all that you can be."

While the students took sure and steady steps toward success, the school was struggling financially. The enrollment increased to nine, but there were often times when the children's parents could not pay tuition. The bills mounted steadily, and both Marva and her husband Clarence took other jobs to try to pay them. On top of these problems, they were told that the school would have to move or be completely rewired to meet fireproofing regulations.

Clarence worked feverishly trying to budget their income to pay the ever-increasing bills. Finally he gave up in frustration and announced to Marva that there would be no Westside Preparatory School the next year.

---

jive talk—*slang words*

"We have come so far! We are really teaching, and the students are learning. After all of the work, why should we quit now?"

"Honey, we are in serious trouble if we do not begin to pay off some of these bills. We could lose the school, our house, and our car. We do not have any money, so we do not have any choice!"

Sighing deeply, Marva went up to her beloved classroom and sat down in one of the old, worn-out desks that Clarence had bought for two dollars apiece. She remembered the day that he had driven into the yard with desks strapped to the top and sides of their car. There had even been desk parts sticking out of the windows. Silently and alone, she sat in the darkness, thinking about the past, the present, and the ominous future.

The next morning, Marva stood before the class and quietly handed a fuel bill to Martin, who gravely looked at it and passed it to the next student. In an unfamiliar, faltering voice, Marva explained that running a school took a great amount of money, and that if this and other bills could not be paid, she would have to close the school. As she looked at each of her students and thought of their progress after only one year of hard work, her voice began to strengthen with hope and her eyes regained their fire.

"But as sure as there is a God in Heaven, we will find a way! Meanwhile, I want to get four hundred dollars worth of learning out of you today. Now who wants to recite this poem first?"

As Marva taught, she did not hear the young man who knocked on the open screen door. Not getting an answer, he went inside and walked up the wooden steps, passed by the peeling wallpaper, and stopped outside the classroom. His large frame filled the doorway as he looked around at the bookshelves that sagged with books and compositions, the bulletin boards that were covered with clippings and charts, and the much-used chalkboards that were almost white with chalk dust. He listened with amazement to the young children's responsiveness and evident self-respect.

"Mrs. Collins, there's a man in the hallway," a young girl in the back row announced suspiciously.

Marva assigned the class some work to do and walked into the hall to meet the man, who introduced himself as Zay Smith, a newspaper columnist for the *Chicago Sun-Times*. He reminded Marva that she had written him a letter and sent him some of her students' papers in response to his article about high school students who had never heard of Shakespeare. "Ma'am, those papers were excellent. I know it has been a long time since you wrote me, but I had to come down and see this place for myself."

"It is only a school, Mr. Smith. No more or no less. Come in and sit for a while if you want."

Marva briefly introduced him to the class and continued teaching. When she eventually dismissed the class, the students groaned with disappointment.

After the students left, Mr. Smith came to the front of the class. "I can't believe it; they really wanted to stay here. How do you do it?"

"Lots of love and hard work, and legs strong enough to get me through each day," answered Marva.

"It has to be more than that!"

"People just won't accept the fact that good old-fashioned teaching still works. It works for everyone—black kids, white kids, rich, poor, purple kids. It works for them all."

"Do you get any money from the government?"

"No," replied Marva. "I teach these children what Marcus Aurelius said—that if you give a man a fish, he will eat for only one day, but if you teach him to fish, he will feed himself for a lifetime. Government money has been used in this neighborhood for many years. People think that someone else must do things for them. These children must learn differently."

The reporter was so impressed by Marva Collins and her students that he wrote a column about them. Word began to spread about Marva Collins the miracle worker. Parent groups called and asked her to speak and paid her hundreds of dollars for her talks about education. Dollars began to come in from supporters, and her story began to spread as magazines and television specials told about her students' success. At the end of the first year, each of Marva's students took an achievement test. The tests showed that they had improved five grade levels—all because of hard work and good teaching. Marva Collins's name was mentioned frequently as a candidate for President Reagan's choice as Secretary of Education. For Marva, however, the opportunity to teach every day in her new, growing school was all she wanted. "I love my children, and I love my school. . . . I wouldn't trade it for a billion dollars," she explained.

Character Theme—Initiative & Sacrifice

Time to Think

1. What were most of the students in Mrs. Collins's first class like?
2. What were some of the hardships that Mrs. Collins faced in her school?
3. How was Mrs. Collins's school different from the public school system?
4. How did Mrs. Collins teach her students to get down the road of success?
5. Describe Marva Collins. What character qualities make her a success?

WHAT IS SUCCESS?

Edgar A. Guest

Success is being friendly when another needs a friend;
It's in the cheery words you speak, and in the coins you lend;
Success is not alone in skill and deeds of daring great;
It's in the roses that you plant beside your neighbor's gate.

Success is in the way you walk the paths of life each day;
It's in the little things you do and in the things you say;
Success is in the glad hello you give your fellow man;
It's in the laughter of your home and all the joys you plan.

Success is not in getting rich or rising high to fame;
It's not alone in winning goals which all men hope to claim;
It's in the man you are each day, through happiness or care;
It's in the cheery words you speak and in the smile you wear.

Success is being big of heart and clean and broad of mind;
It's being faithful to your friends, and to the stranger, kind;
It's in the children whom you love, and all they learn from you—
Success depends on character and everything you do.

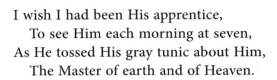

IN THE CARPENTER SHOP

Author Unknown

I wish I had been His apprentice,
    To see Him each morning at seven,
As He tossed His gray tunic about Him,
    The Master of earth and of Heaven.

When He lifted the lid of His workchest,
    And opened His carpenter's kit,
And looked at His chisels and augers,
    And took the bright tools out of it;

When He gazed at the rising sun tinting
    The dew on the opening flowers,
And He smiled at the thought of His Father
    Whose love floods this fair world of ours;

When He fastened the apron about Him,
    And put on His workingman's cap,
And grasped the smooth haft of His hammer
    To give the bent woodwork a tap,

Saying, "Lad, let us finish this ox yoke;
    The farmer must finish his crop."
Oh, I wish I had been His apprentice
    And worked in the Nazareth shop.

But, still as of old we may serve Him,
    For did not the Carpenter say,—
"Inasmuch . . ." as ye aid My littlest one,
    Ye do it, My friend, for Me.

---

chisels—*metal tools used to cut and shape wood*
augers—*tools used to drill holes in wood*

Jungle Pilot

Russell T. Hitt

This true story takes place in the jungles of Ecuador. Nate Saint is the American missionary "jungle pilot" who helps other missionaries and who longs to take the gospel to the savage Auca Indians. The following adventure occurs before Nate meets the Aucas. The inspiring story of how Nate and four fellow missionaries gave their lives for the Aucas is written in the book *Through Gates of Splendor*.

Nate Saint recorded in vivid detail the events of that day:

"I looked at my watch and I said, 'Do you know, Roj, we're not really through—we're still in a rush, man.' The sun was sinking fast, the shadows high on the trees. The air was getting cooler by the minute.

"Roj started grabbing his stuff. I said, 'No, Roj, we can't take one extra pound.' I did let him take his syringe and his camera. The rest of his stuff we threw in a gunnysack and tossed to the chief until we could get back.

"We headed for the airplane, fired the thing up, checked the engine well and started the take-off run. A bump tossed us into the air at about the 160-yard point. After that we touched the turf once more, lightly, then we were airborne."

Nate explained to Roger that he had just enough gas in the tank to make Wambimi, a place where prospecting crews of the Shell Oil Company had abandoned some shacks and an airstrip a few years before. The strip at Wambimi was on the edge of the Atshuara territory about halfway to Macuma. Roger and

---

syringe—*a metal instrument used to inject medicine into the body*
Wambimi (wäm·bē′mē)

Atshuara (ăt·shoo·är′ä)
Macuma (mä·coo′mä)

Barbara had fixed up the strip at Wambimi and spent some time there in outstation work among the Jívaros in that area.

"Frank is waiting for us at Wambimi," Nate explained. "We've got some gas there in a jeep can. Didn't want any extra weight for the landing at Santiaku's place."

"You'll never know how hard we worked," Roger said.

"Brother, you don't need to say a word," Nate said, "your face says it better than any of Mr. Webster's words ever could."

"For a while I thought you weren't going to land," Roger confessed. "Thought you'd throw me the medicine and beat it for home. I nearly died at the thought. Don't know if I could have made it another day."

"I almost did pass you up," Nate agreed. "That isn't exactly what you'd call an airstrip yet. But I knew you'd be needing to get out of there."

Nate's record continues:

"Roger was slumped in the seat, his eyes closed, obviously letting the fatigue drain out of his worn body. Then he opened his eyes again and asked me how come I had so much trouble finding the place this time. I told him I couldn't understand it myself at first. Thought I had that spot nailed. But finally figured it was because I had never been over that country in the late afternoon before. The shadow patterns were all different at that time of day.

"On the way to Wambimi I reeled out the antenna to call in the good word and what do you know—the receiver had gone out. But the transmitter was working, so from there on over to Wambimi I transmitted, repeating several times, that I had Roj with me and we were both headed for Wambimi. Well, it was a beautiful clear evening and I found we'd have time to land, dump in five gallons of gas and the three of us could get on to Macuma

---

Jívaros (hē′vä·rōs)—*South American Indians*
Santiaku (sän·tē·ä′kōo)

before dark. So we really rolled. Landed straight in at Wambimi, cut the engine as soon as we were on the ground, rolled up toward where Frank was waiting. Before we got stopped I shouted to Frank: 'Get the gear. Get the gas and the gear. We've got to get out of here fast.'

"We got the gas in the tank, piled the other stuff in, and we piled in after it. At the end of the strip I stopped and tried the engine. It accelerated rapidly—then cut out. Well, that did it! If everything had been fine, why we probably would have made it on to Macuma, but as it was, we thanked God we were on the ground and not in the air. I told the fellows, 'It's no soap; I think we're here for the night.'

"There was only one thing I could think of doing to that engine, so I got out the tools. It was getting dark fast. I couldn't get the plug out of the carburetor, or the float-chamber drain because the engine was so hot—it was really hot—because we'd come in there plenty fast.

"The wrench wouldn't budge it. We knew we were there for the night anyway, so we decided to let it go till morning.

"While we were waiting, we got to thinking over our situation. It wasn't particularly ideal. We had no flashlight aboard, and through a chain of circumstances we didn't have the emergency kit in the airplane. I might say right here those missing items caused me to make some powerful resolutions for the future. We didn't even have the means of starting a fire.

"We were all in a good mood. The Lord had certainly been good to us, getting us out of that place with no accident—and the medicine that got in there in the nick of time to save those lives. And this whole thing will probably open the door over there in that country to the gospel.

"The abandoned Shell Company shacks were down the strip and off to one side—somewhere out there in the dark. Roj and Frank had both camped there at various times doing outstation work. So when they decided we ought to spend the night in

66

the buildings—well, I didn't give them a hard time; what with a bunch of bugs swarming around us and the evening starting to get really cool, I was game for anything they wanted to do.

"So we started for the shacks. Frank and his wife Marie had been there last and Frank said they had left some provisions locked up in a room. We needed to get a fire going, but what we needed most of all was a light. And by Harry, a light is a light; there is no darkness like darkness.

"Well, these two characters I was with scattered down the trail a way. I didn't know whether they were guiding me or just trying to get themselves down the trail as fast as possible. In the darkness all I could see was their white shirts. It seemed to me that they were practically running. Roj was in the lead, swinging a machete back and forth in the grass to wake up any snakes and get them out of the way. But he was going so fast, I don't know how a snake would have had time to clear out of his way. Apparently he knew the path quite well and he was really making knots. With a little stumbling around, off the edge of the path now and then, we finally got down to the shack.

"It wasn't a welcome little cabin in the woods, with a candle in the window, unfortunately. It was a grim kind of thing there in the gloom. We got inside and it was really dark, no sky at all in there, and Frank reached out a hand in the dark and I got hold of his hand and he guided me through a narrow doorway from one room into another and led me to a chair. I was happy to sit down and stay put. And I just wished like everything that there was some way to reproduce the dialogue I heard as I sat there in the darkness, listening to those two fellows rummaging around, stumbling over stuff, discussing whether to just bash down the door to the locked room, or take it off the hinges, or to work on the lock with a piece of pipe or just what they'd do. Well, it was something like the old radio dramas that I used to

---

machete (mə·shĕt′ē)—*a large knife with a broad blade*

listen to when I was a kid; Bobby Benson and the cowboys going into dark caves. Then I heard something give way—Roj said, 'The top hinge is loose.' Then about that time the whole door came off and I heard them walk into the room. The room had a cement floor. It was an old shower room in the Shell days and this was one of the very few buildings that were still surviving in some sort of decent shape. The others were all decayed and grown over with trees and vines. I heard them moving around in the room and I heard Frank say, 'Look Roj, how do we keep from stepping on the snakes in this place?'

"And Roj said, 'Don't worry about that: I fixed this room up so that it's snake-proof. There's a hole over in the corner. I put a board over that the last time I was here.' There was a moment of absolute silence. Then Frank said, kind of quiet and humblelike, 'I took that board off when I was here; I didn't know what it was for.'

"Well, the thing went on like that. It was so dark I couldn't see my hand in front of my face. I heard tin cans rattling around. And Frank called, 'Roj, come over here and feel in this can; see if you can find some matches.' And Roj said, 'What's the matter with you? I'm not sticking *my* hand down in that thing.' He was afraid there might be a scorpion in it. I don't know whose hand went in the can, but at any rate, they kept rattling cans and announcing what they thought they were finding. The lid came off one can and Roj said, 'This is coffee!' Another can would be lentils, another can of beans, dried beans, but no matches. Finally Frank said, 'Here's a matchbox.' He had found a matchbox somewhere, but when he opened it, it had nails in it. What a disappointment. It was getting miserably cold. We had one blanket with us. I got hold of it and was wrapped up sitting in my chair, listening to this dialogue and thinking of the humorous side of the situation, which would seem a lot more

---

lentils—*small, round, edible beanlike seeds*   scorpion—*a poisonous, insectlike creature*

humorous if we could find a match or two. Then Roj stumbled on an old radio B battery, which might have enough voltage left to make a spark. They had already found a little tin of kerosene and another of gasoline. Maybe if that battery would make a spark I could light some gasoline. It was a long shot, but it just might work. So I felt my way over and got hold of this battery. They finally found a little piece of wire and they handed it to me so I went back to my chair and huddled up in this blanket. I was fiddling around Braille method, trying to find the outlets on the battery to stick those wires in and see if I could produce a spark.

"While I was doing that Roj walked over and without changing his tone at all, said, 'Take heart, boys, I've got some matches.' I couldn't believe it; I thought he was kidding us until I saw that match flare. And I'm telling you, that match had as much light in it as a 100-watt bulb, there in that darkness. Boy, it was a beautiful bright light just flooding that whole room; but I was sort of afraid he would let the thing go out, and maybe

there wouldn't be any more matches, or they'd be wet, or something. Then they found a few candles, a whole box of them as a matter of fact, and the first thing you know, they had several candles going and we had light all over the place.

"We quickly found there in the storeroom canned preserves, a quart of beef, succotash, pears, pickled beets, and some other things. We marched triumphantly off to the kitchen in the other end of the shack.

"There we found a couple of plates and a big wooden spoon. We bent jar lids to make two more spoons. Frank put a handful of lentils in a pot of water, and we got a fire going in the stove—a brick stove with a sheet of metal over it. We made a stew out of the succotash and meat. The stew really went down well, slid right down. We heated up some water in a tin can and threw some coffee in it, and that coffee went down very nicely. We found a jar of sugar and, boy, just everything you could ask for. It was just like the Lord had prepared a table before us in the presence of our enemies. There it was—and our cup was surely running over. No meal was ever more appreciated, I'm sure. Especially for Roj—although he did say that the Indians fed him pretty well over there. Even though most of them were sick, they saw to it that he got well fed."

Roger told his two missionary teammates of the frantic days in Santiaku's village, of the sickness, and how one key man of the tribe had died the day before he arrived.

Roger kept saying, "The Lord was in this whole thing! We've got a solid opening with those fellows and we can get in there now with the gospel."

"We had our last cup of coffee around midnight," Nate recorded, "then it was time to turn in. We had one blanket and had to sleep Indian style, three on one big chonta wood bed. I'm not a very good double-sleeper, but I was almost beyond feeling

---

chonta—*a type of palm tree*

70

by that time, so I crawled in between those two characters on the hard chonta boards, double-sleeper or no."

The boys were up at five-thirty and Nate soon had the airplane fixed. He flew it first alone, then loaded in the others and the extra paraphernalia, and, as Nate described it, "We took off and made a bee-line for Macuma, and when we got to Macuma people were pretty glad to see people—on both sides of the fence."

A few minutes later Nate took off alone for Shell Mera. It was still early on that beautiful Sunday morning. He loved to fly the airplane empty—without its usual capacity load it climbed so fast and free into the clear blue sky. He recorded the special thrill he got that morning at seeing the snow-capped peaks, Tungurahua and El Altar in the distance as he flew toward his home base in the foothills. He saw Chimborazo (two hundred miles away) and the active volcano Sangay.

It was time for summarizing, a time for reflection. He would get someone with more medicine back into the Atshuara village, probably tomorrow. And the Indians would hear the gospel and have their eyes turned toward Calvary.

Nate was glad to be a part of the overall missionary effort in this remote part of God's vineyard. He had come to Ecuador as a pilot for a growing organization known as the Missionary Aviation Fellowship. MAF had been started by a small group of World War II pilots. These dedicated young men, with rare vision, had foreseen what airplanes and radio could do to extend the arms of missionaries in out-of-the-way places. Their little yellow planes, better adapted to tiny jungle airstrips than larger planes, were active in the skies over many countries.

Nate Saint was one of the earliest of MAF's circuit riders, his parish covering an ever-increasing number of Protestant mission stations in the eastern jungle of Ecuador. His was the task

paraphernalia—*equipment*   **Chimborazo** (chĕm·bō·rä′zō)
Tungurahua (tōōng′gōō·rä′wä)

71

of providing logistic support for the missionaries who labored patiently in their lonely outposts, taking in mail, fresh meat and vegetables, and all the hundred and one items needed for jungle living. He took in medicine and flew the sick out to a doctor.

Nate was a pilot and a mechanic, but he was a missionary too, one in mind and spirit with the missionary families of the jungle. Some time before he had written of his feeling for the pioneering missionaries he loved to serve:

"Their call of God is to the regions beyond the ends of civilization's roads—where there is no other form of transportation. They have probed the frontiers to the limit of physical capacity and prayed for a means of reaching the regions beyond—a land of witch doctors and evil spirits—a land where the woman has no soul; she's just a beast of burden—a land where there's no word for love in their vocabulary—no word to express the love of a father for his son. In order to reach these people for whom Christ died, pioneer missionaries slug it out on the jungle trails

logistic—*having to do with the distribution, maintenance, and replacement of supplies*

72

day after day, sometimes for weeks, often in mud up to their knees, while up above them the towering tropical trees push upward in a never-ending struggle for light.

"It is our task," Nate's record continues, "to lift those missionaries up off those rigorous, life-consuming, and morale-breaking jungle trails—lift them up to where five minutes in a plane equals twenty-four hours on foot. The reason for all this is not a matter of bringing comfort to the missionaries. They don't go to the steaming, tropical jungles looking for comfort in the first place. It's a matter of gaining precious time, of redeeming days and weeks, months and even years that can be spent in giving the Word of Life to primitive people."

Winging toward Shell Mera on that crystal-clear Sunday morning, Nate Saint's gaze swept the horizon to the northeastward where lived the savage Auca Indians, a Stone Age tribe who kill swiftly and silently from ambush—a tribe which no white man or Indian had entered peacefully in more than three

---

morale—*good spirits such as confidence, cheerfulness, willingness, etc.*

primitive—*not in keeping with modern civilization*

hundred years. Nate's heart went out to those unknown wraiths of the jungle. They too were men for whom Christ died. "Some one of these days we'll find a way to reach them too," Nate thought to himself.

Character Theme—Sacrifice, Faith,
& Service

Time to Think

1. Where does this true story take place?
2. Why did Nate and Roj and Frank have to spend the night at Wambimi?
3. When Nate realized they would have to spend the night at Wambimi, he said he made some powerful resolutions for the future. What do you think he meant?
4. What did you learn about being a missionary from this story?
5. Nate Saint did finally meet the Auca Indians of Ecuador, the people for whom God had given him a burden. The Indians killed him and four other missionary men. Years later, some of those same Auca Indians came to know Christ through the prayers and work of the families of the dead missionaries. Was Nate Saint a "winner" or a "loser"?

The Picture That Thrilled the Nation

J. Campbell Bruce

Joe Rosenthal, a 33-year-old cameraman, climbed an extinct volcano on an island speck in the Pacific and snapped an action shot. "That ought to make a good picture—if I caught it," he thought.

Every American soon knew he had caught it. Perfect in composition, the photo of the flag-raising at Iwo Jima was the *Spirit of '76* in modern combat-dress. It has since been reproduced more than any other photograph in history. It has inspired poems, paintings, statues, pageants. On the banks of the Potomac stands a 75-foot-high re-creation of the scene in bronze, the gift of the Marine Corps to the American people.

The photographer who snapped that historic picture was five-foot-five and nearsighted. An Associated Press cameraman

---

Iwo Jima (ē′wə jē′mə)—*an island in the western Pacific*

in San Francisco when the Japanese attacked Pearl Harbor, he tried to join up at once, but the Army, the Navy, the Marines, and the Seabees turned him down for vision only one-twentieth of normal. It was not until 1944 that he got to the Pacific as an AP photographer. Peering through thick-lensed glasses, Joe Rosenthal covered the several campaigns. He made D-day landings with both the Marines and the Army.

Joe got to Iwo Jima soon after the first assault wave, carrying, as always, two extra pairs of eyeglasses. He moved in with his unit under heavy fire. A cliff to the right bristled with mortars, and snipers infested the terraced slope ahead. Our own planes and Navy pounded the island, and blasts from shore reached out for the landing craft.

Two of Joe's early Iwo Jima photos were acclaimed by his editors: Marines plunging through the rough surf behind others going into battle; Marines in foxholes along a slope below a pillbox they had just knocked out. Between pictures Joe helped lug a stretcher through the shell-geysered surf to the small boats. Once a Marine fell dead four feet ahead of him; once a spent shell fragment landed in his lap.

On the morning of the flag picture, while transferring from command ship to landing craft, Joe fell into the water and was nearly crushed between the two craft. He lost his helmet, but fortunately he had already handed over his cameras.

As the boat churned shoreward the coxswain shouted: "They're going to plant the flag on Mount Suribachi. See that red spot part way up? That's them taking it up."

Suribachi, a 560-foot volcanic cone, stood at the southern tip of the island. The Stars and Stripes flying at its summit would boost the morale of the forces fighting on the plain to the north.

---

campaigns—*military operations*
assault wave—*an attack that is part of a series of attacks*

pillbox—*a platform for a machine gun*
coxswain—*man who steers a ship's boat*
Mount Suribachi (sŏŏr·ĭ·bä′chē)

Rosenthal splashed ashore, donned the dented, fire-blackened helmet of a dead Marine, stepped gingerly through a marked mine field, and started up the 45-degree slope strewn with the dead. Frequently a shout rang out—"Down!"—as a Marine tossed a grenade into a dugout and leaped aside, just above the clambering photographer.

When Joe got to the top a small flag was already flying. Fifty feet away, on the very crest of Suribachi, huddled five Marines and a Navy corpsman—the group he had seen from the boat. They were attaching ropes to the flagstaff, a 20-foot iron pipe.

Joe strode over. "What's doing?"

"We're going to put this up and keep the other as a souvenir," said a Marine who was cradling in his arms a much larger American flag, which would be readily seen from anywhere on the island.

Joe studied the layout. To take in the tall flagstaff as it went up, he had to move back 35 feet. He set the shutter speed. The pole swung upward—and Joe clicked his shutter at exactly the right split second.

Joe hitched a ride to the command ship, typed out captions and dispatched the films to Guam. He didn't know it, but he had made the war's greatest picture.

Within 24 hours of its taking, the picture had thrilled millions of Americans. It was soon compared to "Washington Crossing the Delaware." Sunday supplements carried it full page in color, next to Archibald Willard's painting "The Spirit of '76 Marches On." Joe's draft board proudly reclassified him.

Unaware of all this, Joe received a pay raise, and then two days later a radio message calling him home. Joe replied he had another beachhead coming up. Associated Press shot back: "This is an order, not a request."

Joe Rosenthal landed in San Francisco a celebrity. People pounded him on the back and said, "Joe, you shouldn't take such risks." He went on to New York and a dazzling round of banquets, speech-making, interviews, and honors. He won the Pulitzer Prize and other top awards, and became the world's most photographed photographer. Pressed for a comment on the picture, he said quietly, "I like it. I think it reflects credit on the Marines."

As a three-cent stamp, the photo broke all post office records for "First Day of Issue," prized by stamp collectors. It was re-created in paintings, statues, medallions—in oils, pastels, watercolors, stone, bronze, plaster, wood, even in ice for a San Francisco banquet. Joe was given a bonus—a year's salary in war bonds.

A promoter offered Joe $200,000 for all rights. He referred the promoter to the AP, which holds the copyright and keeps the original negative locked up. But from the first the AP has barred its use commercially, quietly turning over all proceeds from reprint and copy sales to the Navy Relief Society.

The flag is now in the Marine Corps museum at Quantico, Va., and a bronze copy of the photo is embedded in a monument atop Mount Suribachi. A plaque awarded to Joe Rosenthal by the Catholic Institute of the Press hangs in the AP lobby in New York, bearing this tribute:

> *Faith in God was his armor,*
> *His weapons valor and skill.*
> *He served in the best tradition of*
> *   the American press photographer.*

Character Theme—Initiative, Courage, &
Patriotism

Time to Think

1. Why was Joe Rosenthal unable to join the military?
2. What quality did Joe have that helped him overcome his difficulty?
3. What was the purpose for raising a large flag atop Mount Suribachi?
4. Why do you think that Joe Rosenthal's picture became so popular? Do you like it for those same reasons?
5. Reread the tribute written on Joe Rosenthal's plaque. Do you see what made him a success?

The Flag of Our Country

Charles Sumner

There is the national flag. He must be cold indeed who can look upon its folds, rippling in the breeze, without pride of country. If he be in a foreign land, the flag is companionship and country itself, with all its endearments.

Who, as he sees it, can think of a state merely? Whose eyes, once fastened upon its radiant trophies, can fail to recognize the image of the whole nation? It has been called a "floating piece of poetry," and yet I know not if it has an intrinsic beauty beyond other ensigns. Its highest beauty is in what it symbolizes. It is because it represents all, that all gaze at it with delight and reverence.

It is a piece of bunting lifted in the air; but it speaks sublimely, and every part has a voice. Its stripes of alternate red and white proclaim the original union of thirteen states to maintain the Declaration of Independence. Its stars of white on a field of blue, proclaim that union of states constituting our national constellation, which receives a new star with every new state. The two together signify union past and present.

The very colors have a language which was officially recognized by our fathers. White is for purity, red for valor, blue for justice; and all together—bunting, stripes, stars, and colors, blazing in the sky—make the flag of our country to be cherished by all our hearts, to be upheld by all our hands.

---

intrinsic—*natural*

Character Theme—Patriotism

Early Summer Thought

Marie J. Post

God gives so much of beauty
No day is common fare.
If we but took the time to look,
Some loveliness is there.

Regret not Spring's departure,
June dawns with clover field.
Along each way, through every day
Some beauty is revealed.

Cheerfulness

Margaret Slattery

There once lived a woman who thought she had the very hardest cross in all the world. No one suffered as she did, she thought, and no one was as lonely as she. Her eyes were often filled with tears. Her whole attitude cast a gloom over all who came near, and people began to avoid her. One night as she lay thinking about it with great bitterness in her heart, comparing her heavily burdened life with the lives of other women she knew, she heard a voice saying, "You may exchange your cross. See!" And she seemed to see a great room all of marble pure and white, and around on the walls hung crosses of every size and made of every sort of material.

"There," said the voice, "exchange your cross. Each of these belongs to someone in the world. Many, like you, desire an easy one. All must have something in life that is hard; no one escapes. But if your cross seems indeed unbearable, choose another."

Gladly she went about the room trying the crosses. They were so deceptive! The tiniest one, which she thought would be so easy, seemed like iron as she tried to carry it. And one of gold, that looked very beautiful and bore many jewels, hurt so deeply that she laid it quickly aside.

All night she tested the crosses, and when the gray morning light came into the marble room, she went to the man at the door and said, "Oh, sir, I pray you, sir, give me back my own cross." The man whose voice had spoken to her in the night drew his robe about him, smiled, and answered, "That is what all say who enter here. Take it, and bear it courageously."

It is a story, a dream, but it is true. If we realize the great fact that all suffer, all have difficulties and trials, all have longings unsatisfied, and that there is no reason why we should escape, it will help hush the word of complaint upon our lips and change the frown to a smile.

There are two kinds of people in the world, those who see clouds, and those who see through the clouds. Each one of us has to decide for himself to which class he will belong.

Those who look through the clouds, be they soft and filmy or heavy and dark, see the sun. It is there. It is always there, always shining. They know that clouds always move on, and they wait, hoping that today they may pass; if not today, then surely tomorrow. And tomorrow they have the same hope, and at last the day comes when the sun in all its glory shines upon them.

These are the people it is good to meet in homes and schoolrooms, in offices and shops, behind counters and on street corners—everywhere in the world.

They are the ones who should be awarded a medal or a prize in gold—all those who meet the world with a cheerful face and a voice that makes all hard things seem easier because of the note of faith and hope there is in it. They are the ones without whom happiness would be impossible. One can no more think of life without these smiling faces than of a world without air, with no stars and no sun.

Out in the world are clouds, hard things as well as easy. No one wishes to be deceived about that—and out there cheerfulness is a great asset. Secure it—at any price.

Character Theme—Contentment

Time to Think

1. Do you think the woman in this story changed after her dream? How do you think she was different?
2. Why is it important for you to be cheerful?

A Father's Prayer

Douglas MacArthur

In early 1942, when leading outnumbered United States forces in the Philippines, the late General Douglas MacArthur prayed this prayer many times at morning devotions, according to Major General Courtney Whitney, his long-time military aide. This prayer for his son, Arthur, is a spiritual legacy any son would cherish.

Build me a son, O Lord, who will be strong enough to know when he is weak, and brave enough to face himself when he is afraid; one who will be proud and unbending in honest defeat, and humble and gentle in victory.

Build me a son whose wishes will not take the place of deeds; a son who will know Thee—and that to know himself is the foundation stone of knowledge.

Lead him, I pray, not in the path of ease and comfort, but under the stress and spur of difficulties and challenge. Here let him learn to stand up in the storm; here let him learn compassion for those who fail.

Build me a son whose heart will be clear, whose goal will be high; a son who will master himself before he seeks to master other men; one who will reach into the future, yet never forget the past.

And after all these things are his, add, I pray, enough of a sense of humor, so that he may always be serious, yet never take himself too seriously. Give him humility, so that he may always remember the simplicity of true greatness, the open mind of true wisdom, and the meekness of true strength.

Then I, his father, will dare to whisper, "I have not lived in vain."

Character Theme—Prayer & Wisdom

Wit and Wisdom
of Mark Twain

MEET THE AUTHOR

Samuel Clemens, who is better known by his pseudonym "Mark Twain," is one of America's most famous writers. Mr. Clemens spent his boyhood along the Mississippi River in the small town of Hannibal, Missouri. Hannibal became famous to people around the world as the setting for Twain's novels of boyhood memories, *Tom Sawyer* and *Huckleberry Finn*.

Mark Twain is well known for his stories like "The Celebrated Jumping Frog of Calaveras County." Here are some examples of Mark Twain's wit and wisdom.

◆ It's better to keep your mouth shut and appear stupid than to open it and remove all doubt.

◆ Let us endeavor so to live that when we come to die even the undertaker will be sorry.

◆ The principal difference between a cat and a lie is that a cat has only 9 lives.

◆ In India "cold weather" is merely a conventional phrase and has come into use through the necessity of having some way to distinguish between weather which will melt a brass doorknob and weather which will only make it mushy.

◆ Noise proves nothing. Often a hen who has merely laid an egg cackles as if she has laid an asteroid.

◆ Wrinkles should merely indicate where the smiles have been.

◆ The reports of my death are greatly exaggerated.

Character Theme—Wisdom

The Maxims of Poor Richard

Benjamin Franklin

The wise sayings that Benjamin Franklin published in his *Poor Richard's Almanac* during our colonial days have guided many generations of Americans toward success in their daily endeavors.

- Little strokes fell great oaks.
- God helps them that help themselves.
- The sleeping fox catches no poultry.
- He that rises late must trot all day.
- There are no gains without pains.
- Diligence is the mother of good luck.
- One today is worth two tomorrows.
- Be ashamed to catch yourself idle.
- If you would have your business done, go; if not, send.
- Think of saving as well as of getting.
- Always taking out of the meal tub and never putting in soon comes to the bottom.
- He that goes a-borrowing goes a-sorrowing.
- 'Tis hard for an empty bag to stand upright.
- Experience keeps a dear school, but fools will learn in no other.
- If you will not hear reason she will surely rap your knuckles.
- He that can have patience can have what he will.
- Search others for their virtues, thyself for thy vices.
- Early to bed and early to rise, makes a man healthy, wealthy, and wise.
- Have you somewhat to do tomorrow? Do it today.
- Constant dropping wears away stones.

***Character Theme*—Wisdom**

---

poultry—*birds raised for meat or eggs, such as chickens*
dear—*having a high price*
rap (knuckles)—*to hit quickly*

Wolf
The Faithful Collie

Albert Terhune

MEET THE AUTHOR

Albert Payson Terhune (1872–1942) is remembered for his wonderful stories and books about dogs, usually his own collies.

People loved the dogs in his stories so much and were so curious about them that newspapers sometimes reported on them for their readers. In 1923, the *New York Times* printed a long account of the death of Wolf, the dog you will be reading about in the following story.

Mr. Terhune's first book was the story of Wolf's father, entitled *Lad: A Dog*.

Wolf was a collie, red-gold and white of coat, with a shape more like that of his long-ago wolf ancestors than like a domesticated dog's shape. It was from this fact that he was named Wolf.

He looked not at all like his great sire, Lad, nor like his dainty, thoroughbred mother, Lady. Nor was he like them in any other way, except that he inherited old Lad's gallant spirit and loyalty. No, in traits as well as in looks, he was more wolf than dog. He almost never barked, his snarl supplying all vocal needs.

The mistress or the master or the boy—any of these three could romp with him, roll him over, and tickle him; and Wolf entered gleefully into the fun of the romp. But, let any human besides these three lay a hand on his slender body, and a snarling plunge for the offender's throat was Wolf's reply.

It had been so since his puppyhood. He did not fly at guests, nor, indeed, pay any heed to their presence, so long as they kept their hands off him. But to all of these the boy was forced to say at the outset of the visit:

---

domesticated—*tame*   sire—*father*

"Pat Lad and Bruce all you want to, but leave Wolf alone. He doesn't care for people." Then the boy would proceed to tumble Wolf about, to the delight of both.

In romping with humans whom they love, most dogs will bite more or less gently, or pretend to bite, as a part of the game. Wolf never did. In his wildest and roughest romps with the boy or with the boy's parents, Wolf did not so much as open his mighty jaws—perhaps because he realized that a bite was not a joke, but an effort to kill.

There had been only one exception to Wolf's hatred for mauling at strangers' hands. A man came to The Place on a business call, bringing with him a two-year-old daughter. The master warned the baby that she must not go near Wolf, although she might pet any of the other collies. Then he became so much interested in the business talk that he and his guest forgot all about the child.

Ten minutes later, the master chanced to shift his gaze to the far end of the room, and he broke off with a gasp, in the very middle of a sentence.

The baby was seated astride Wolf's back, her tiny heels digging into the dog's ribs, and each of her chubby fists gripping one of his ears. Wolf was lying there, with a happy grin on his face and wagging his tail in joy.

No one knew why he had yielded to the baby's tugging hands, except because she was a baby, and because the gallant heart of the dog had gone out to her helplessness.

Wolf was the official watchdog of The Place, and his name carried dread to the loafers and tramps of

mauling—*rough handling*

the region. Also, he was the boy's own dog. He had been born on the boy's tenth birthday, five years before this story of ours begins, and ever since then the two had been chums.

One sloppy afternoon in late winter, Wolf and the boy were sprawled, side by side, on the rug in front of the library fire. The mistress and the master had gone to town for the day. The house was lonely, and the two chums were left to entertain each other.

The boy was reading a magazine. The dog beside him was blinking in drowsy comfort at the fire. Presently, finishing the story he had been reading, the boy looked across at the sleepy dog.

"Wolf," he said, "here's a story about a dog. I think he must have been something like you. Maybe he was your great-great-great-great grandfather, because he lived an awfully long time ago—in Pompeii. Ever hear of Pompeii?"

Now, the boy was fifteen years old, and he had too much sense to imagine that Wolf could possibly understand the story he was about to tell him; but long since, he had fallen into the way of talking to his dog, sometimes as if to a person. It was fun for him to note the eagerness wherewith Wolf listened and tried to grasp the meaning of what he was saying. Again and again, at the sound of some familiar word or tone of voice, the collie would prick up his ears or wag his tail, as if in the joyous hope that he had at last found a clue to the owner's meaning.

"You see," went on the boy, "this dog lived in Pompeii, as I told you. You've never been there, Wolf."

Wolf was looking up at the boy in wistful excitement, seeking to guess what was expected of him.

"And," continued the boy, "the kid who owned him seems to have had a regular knack of getting into trouble all the time. His dog was always on hand to get him out of it. It's a true story, the

---

Pompeii (pŏm·pā′)—*an Italian city destroyed when Mt. Vesuvius erupted in A.D. 79*

magazine says. The kid's father was so grateful to the dog that he bought him a solid silver collar. Solid silver! Get that, Wolfie?"

Wolf did not "get it," but he wagged his tail hopefully, his eyes bright with interest.

"And," said the boy, "what do you suppose was engraved on the collar! Well, I'll tell you: 'This dog has thrice saved his little master from death. Once by fire, once by flood, and once at the hands of robbers!' How's that for a record, Wolf? For one dog, too!"

At the words "Wolf" and "dog" the collie's tail beat on the floor. Then he moved closer to the boy, whose voice soon took on a sadder note.

"But at last," said the boy, "there came a time when the dog couldn't save the kid. Mount Vesuvius erupted. All the sky was pitch-dark, as black as midnight, and the city of Pompeii was buried under lava and ashes. The dog might have got away by himself—dogs can see in the dark, can't they, Wolf?—but he couldn't get the kid away. And he wouldn't go without him. You wouldn't have gone without me, either, would you, Wolf? Pretty nearly two thousand years later some people dug through the lava that covered Pompeii. What do you suppose they found? Of course they found a whole lot of things. One of them was that dog—silver collar and all. He was lying at the feet of a child. It must have been the child he couldn't save. He was one grand dog—hey, Wolf?"

The continued strain of trying to understand began to get on the collie's high-strung nerves. He rose to his feet, quivering, and sought to lick the boy's face, thrusting one upraised white forepaw at him for a handshake. The boy slammed shut the magazine.

"It's slow in the house, here, with nothing to do," he said to his chum. "I'm going to the lake with my gun to see if any wild ducks have landed in the marshes yet. It's almost time for them. Want to come along?"

The last sentence Wolf understood perfectly. On the instant, he was dancing with excitement at the prospect of a walk. Being a collie he was of no earthly help in a hunting trip; but on such tramps, as everywhere else, he was the boy's faithful companion.

Out over the slushy snow the two started, the boy with his single-barreled shotgun slung over one shoulder, the dog trotting close at his heels. The March thaw was changing to a sharp freeze. The deep and soggy snow was crusted over just thick enough to make walking difficult for both dog and boy.

The Place was on a point that ran out into the lake, on the opposite bank from the mile-distant village. Behind, across the highway, lay the winter-choked forest. At the lake's northerly end, two miles beyond The Place, were the marshes where, a month hence, wild duck would gather. Thither, with Wolf, the boy plowed his way through the biting cold.

A quarter of a mile below the marshes the boy struck out across the upper corner of the lake. Here the ice was rotten at the top, but beneath, it was still a full eight inches thick, strong enough to bear the boy's weight.

Along the gray ice field the two plodded. The skim of water, which the thaw had spread an inch thick over the ice, had frozen in the day's cold spell. It crackled like broken glass as the chums walked over it. The boy had on big hunting boots, so the glass-like ice did not bother him. To Wolf it gave sharp pain. The small particles were forever getting between the callous black pads of his feet, pricking and cutting him sharply.

Little smears of blood began to mark the dog's course; but it never occurred to Wolf to turn back, or to betray by any sign that he was suffering. It was all a part of the day's work—a cheap price to pay for the joy of tramping with his adored young master.

---

thither—*toward that place*   rotten—*soft; easily broken*

Then, forty yards or so on the hither side of the marshes, Wolf beheld an amazing thing. The boy had been walking directly in front of him, with his gun over his shoulder. With no warning at all, the youthful hunter fell, feet foremost, through three feet of water and through nearly two feet more of sticky marsh mud that underlay the lake bed.

The light shell of new-frozen water that covered the lake's thicker ice had also concealed an air hole nearly three feet wide. Into this, as he strode carelessly along, the boy had stepped. Straight down he had gone, with all the force of his one hundred ten pounds and with all the strength of his forward stride.

Instinctively he had thrown out his hands to restore his balance. The only effect of this was to send the gun flying ten feet away.

His outflung hands struck against the ice on the edges of the air hole, and clung there. Sputtering and gurgling, the boy brought his head above the surface and tried to raise himself, by his hands, high enough to wriggle out upon the surface of the ice. This would have been simple enough for so strong a lad, but the glue-like mud had imprisoned his feet and the lower part of his legs and held them powerless.

Try as he would, the boy could not wrench himself free. The water, as he stood upright, was on a level with his mouth. The air hole was too wide for him, at such a depth, to get a good hold on its edges and lift himself bodily to safety.

Gaining such a finger hold as he could, he heaved with all his might, throwing every muscle of his body into the struggle. One leg was pulled almost free of the mud, but the other was driven deeper into it. And as the boy's fingers slipped from the smoothly wet ice edge, the attempt to restore his balance drove the free leg back, knee-deep into the mire.

Ten minutes of this hopeless fighting left the boy panting and tired out. The icy water was numbing his nerves and chill-

hither—*near*

92

ing his blood. His hands were without sense of feeling as far up as the wrists. Even if he could have shaken free his legs from the mud, now he had not strength enough left to crawl out of the hole. He ceased his frantic battle and stood dazed. Then he came sharply to himself. For, as he stood, the water crept upward from his lips to his nostrils. He knew why the water seemed to be rising. It was not rising. It was he who was sinking! As soon as he stopped moving, the mud began, very slowly, but very steadily, to suck him downward.

This was not a quicksand, but it was a deep mud bed, and only by constant motion could he avoid sinking farther and farther into it. He had less than two inches to spare at best before the water should fill his nostrils; less than two inches of life, even if he could keep the water down to the level of his lips.

There was a moment of utter panic. Then the boy's brain cleared. His only hope was to keep on fighting—to rest, when he must, for a moment or so, and then to renew his numbed grip on the ice edge and try to pull his feet a few inches higher out of the mud. He must do this as long as his chilled body could be forced into obeying his will.

He struggled again, but with no result in raising himself. A second struggle, however, brought him chin-high above the water. He remembered that some of these earlier struggles had scarce budged him, while others had gained him two or three inches. He wondered why; then turning his head, he realized.

Wolf, as he turned, was just loosing his hold on the wide collar of the boy's mackinaw. His cut forepaws were still braced against a flaw of ragged ice on the air hole's edge, and all his body was tense.

He was dripping wet, too. The boy noted that; and he realized that the repeated effort to draw his master to safety must have resulted, at least once, in pulling the dog down into the water with the floundering boy.

---

mackinaw—*a short woolen coat*

"Once more, Wolfie! Once more!" chattered the boy through teeth that clicked together.

The dog darted forward, caught his grip afresh on the edge of the boy's collar, and tugged with all his fierce strength, growling and whining all the while.

The boy aided the collie's tuggings by a supreme struggle that lifted him higher than before. He was able to get one arm and shoulder above the ice. His numb fingers closed about the limb of a tree which had been washed downstream in the autumn freshets and had been frozen into the lake ice.

With this new hold, and aided by the dog, the boy tried to drag himself out of the hole. But the chill of the water had done its work. He had not the strength to move farther. The mud still sucked at his calves and ankles. The big hunting boots were full of water and seemed to weigh a ton.

He lay there, gasping and chattering. Then, through the gathering twilight, his eyes fell on the gun lying ten feet away.

"Wolf!" he ordered, nodding toward the weapon, "Get it! Get!"

Not in vain had the boy talked to Wolf for years as if the dog were human. At the words and the nod, the collie trotted

freshets—*floods caused by heavy rains*

over to the gun, lifted it by the stock, and hauled it awkwardly along over the bumpy ice to his master, where he laid it down at the edge of the air hole.

The dog's eyes were cloudy with trouble, and he shivered and whined as if with a chill. The water on his thick coat was freezing to a mass of ice. But it was from anxiety that he shivered and not from cold.

Still keeping his numb grasp on the tree branch, the boy balanced himself as best he could, and thrust two fingers of his free hand into his mouth to warm them.

When this was done, he reached out to where the gun lay, and pulled its trigger. The shot boomed deafeningly through the winter silence. The recoil sent the weapon sliding sharply back along the ice, spraining the boy's trigger finger and cutting it to the bone.

"That's all I can do," said the boy to himself. "If anyone hears it, well and good. I can't get at another cartridge. I couldn't put it into the breech if I had to. My hands are too numb."

For several endless minutes he clung there listening. But this was a desolate part of the lake, far from any road, and the season was too early for other hunters to be abroad. The bitter cold, in any case, made sane people hug the fireside rather than venture so far into the open. Nor was the single report of a gun uncommon enough to call forth alarm in such weather.

All this the boy told himself as the minutes dragged by. Then he looked again at Wolf. The dog, head on one side, still stood protectingly above him. The dog was cold and in pain, but being only a dog, it did not occur to him to trot off home to the comfort of the library fire and leave his master to look out for himself.

Presently, with a little sigh, Wolf lay down on the ice, his nose across the boy's arm. Even if he lacked strength to save his beloved master, he could stay and share the boy's sufferings.

---

breech—*the part of a gun behind the barrel*

But the boy himself thought otherwise. He did not intend to freeze to death, nor was he willing to let Wolf imitate the dog of Pompeii by dying helplessly at his master's side. Controlling for an instant the chattering of his teeth, he called, "Wolf!"

The dog was on his feet again at the word, alert, eager.

"Wolf!" repeated the boy. "Go! Hear me? Go!"

He pointed homeward.

Wolf stared at him. Again the boy called, "Go!"

The collie lifted his head to the twilight sky in a wolf howl, hideous in its grief—a howl as wild as that of any of his savage ancestors. Then, stooping first to lick the numb hand that clung to the branch, Wolf turned and fled.

Across the cruelly sharp ice he tore at top speed, head down, whirling through the deepening dusk like a flash of tawny light.

Wolf understood what was wanted of him. Wolf always understood. The pain in his feet was as nothing. The stiffness of his numbed body was forgotten in the need for speed.

The boy looked after the vanishing figure which the dusk was swallowing up. He knew the dog would try to bring help. Whether or not that help could arrive in time, or at all, was a point on which the boy would not let himself dwell. Into his benumbed brain crept the memory of an old Norse proverb he had read in school: "Heroism consists in hanging on one minute longer."

Unconsciously he tightened his feeble hold on the tree branch and braced himself.

From the marshes to The Place was a full two miles. Despite the deep and sticky snow, Wolf covered the distance in less than six minutes. He paused in front of the gate lodge, at the entrance to the drive. But the gardener and his wife had gone to Paterson, shopping, that afternoon.

---

tawny—*brownish yellow*   Norse—*medieval Scandinavian*

Down the drive to the house he dashed. The maids had taken advantage of their employers' day in New York to walk across the lake to the village.

Wise men claim that dogs have not the power to think or to reason things out. So perhaps it was mere chance that next sent Wolf's flying feet across the lake to the village. Perhaps it was chance, and not the knowledge that where there is a village there are people.

Again and again, in the car, he had sat upon the front seat alongside the mistress when she drove to the station to meet guests. There were always people at the station, and to the station Wolf now raced.

The usual group of platform idlers had been driven home by the cold. A baggage man was hauling a trunk and some boxes out of the express room on to the platform to be put aboard the five o'clock train from New York.

As the baggage man passed under the clump of station lights, he came to a sudden halt, for out of the darkness dashed a dog. Full tilt the animal rushed up to him and seized him by the skirt of the overcoat.

The man cried out in scared surprise. He dropped the box he was carrying and struck at the dog to ward off his attack. He recognized Wolf, and he knew the collie's reputation.

But Wolf was not attacking. Holding tight to the coat skirt, he backed away, trying to draw the man with him, and all the time whimpering aloud like a nervous puppy.

A kick from the man's heavy-shod boot broke the dog's hold on the coat, even as a second yell from the man brought four or five other people running out from the station waiting room.

One of these, the telegraph operator, took in the scene at a single glance. With great presence of mind he bawled loudly, "MAD DOG!"

full tilt—*at full speed*

This happened just as Wolf, reeling from the kick, sought to gain another grip on the coat skirt. A second kick sent him rolling over and over on the tracks, while other voices took up the panic cry of "Mad dog!"

Now a mad dog is supposed to be a dog afflicted by rabies. Once in ten thousand times, at the very most, a mad-dog hue-and-cry is justified. Certainly not oftener. A harmless and friendly dog loses his master on the street. He runs about, confused and frightened, looking for the owner he has lost. A boy throws a stone at him. Other boys chase him. His tongue hangs out and his eyes glaze with terror. Then some fool bellows, "Mad dog!"

And the cruel chase is on—a chase that ends in the pitiful victim's death. Yet in every crowd there is a voice ready to raise that cruel shout.

So it was with the men who saw Wolf's frenzied effort to take aid to the endangered boy.

Voice after voice repeated the cry. Men groped along the platform edge for stones to throw, and the village policeman ran upon the scene, drawing his revolver.

Finding it useless to make a further attempt to drag the baggage man to the rescue, Wolf leaped back, facing the ever-larger crowd. Back went his head again in a hideous wolf howl. Then he galloped away a few yards, trotted back, howled once more, and again galloped toward the lake.

All of this only convinced the crowd that they were threatened by a mad dog. A shower of stones fell about Wolf as he came back a third time to influence these dull people into following him.

One pointed rock smote the collie's shoulder, glancing, cutting it to the bone. A shot from the policeman's revolver fanned his fur as it whizzed past.

---

hue-and-cry—*a public outcry*

Knowing that he faced death, he stood his ground, not troubling to dodge the stones, but continuing to run lakeward and then trot back, whining with excitement.

A second pistol shot flew wide. A third grazed the dog's hip. From all directions people were running toward the station. A man darted into a house next door and came out carrying a shotgun.

Just then the train from New York came in, and the sport of "mad-dog" killing was delayed, while the crowd scattered to each side of the track.

From the front car of the train the mistress and the master stepped out into the noise and confusion.

"Better hide in the station, ma'am!" shouted the telegraph operator, at the sight of the mistress. "There is a mad dog loose out there! He's chasing folks around, and—"

"Mad dog!" repeated the mistress. "If you knew anything about dogs, you'd know mad ones never 'chase folks around' any more than typhoid patients do. Then—"

A flash of tawny light beneath the station lamp, a scurrying of frightened idlers, a final wasted shot from the policeman's pistol, as Wolf dived headlong through the frightened crowd toward the voice he heard and recognized.

Up to the mistress and the master galloped Wolf. He was bleeding, his eyes were bloodshot, his fur was rumpled. He seized the master's gloved hand lightly between his teeth and sought to pull him across the tracks toward the lake. The master knew dogs, especially he knew Wolf, and without a word he suffered himself to be led. The mistress and one or two men followed.

Presently Wolf loosed his hold on the master's hand and ran on ahead, darting back every few minutes to make certain he was being followed.

"Heroism—consists—in—hanging—on—one—minute—longer," the boy was whispering to himself for the hundredth time as Wolf pattered up to him in triumph across the ice, with the human rescuers a scant ten yards behind!

Character Theme—Courage & Loyalty

Time to Think

1. In what ways was Wolf more like a wolf than a dog?
2. Describe the walk to the marshes.
3. What caused the boy to fall?
4. Why couldn't the boy climb out since the water was only three feet deep?
5. Explain in your own words the meaning of the proverb, "Heroism consists in hanging on one minute longer."
6. There are two heroes in this story. Who are they? How did they prove to be heroes?

Snobber

Edwin Way Teale

In Vineland, New Jersey, one summer, pedestrians were astonished when an English sparrow darted down from the branches of trees, alighted on their shoulders, and peered intently into their faces. Residents were equally amazed when the same bird flew in at their open windows. It fluttered about, examined their rooms, and flew out again. The mystery grew for several days. Then the following advertisement appeared in the *Vineland Times-Journal*: Lost. Tame female English sparrow. Reward. Call 1291J.

That advertisement brought about the return of a remarkable pet. It also revealed a boy-and-bird companionship which was as interesting as it was unusual. The boy was Bennett Rothenberg; the sparrow, Snobber. They were visiting the boy's uncle near Vineland when the bird became lost.

The boy and the sparrow lived on the eleventh floor of a great apartment building across from the Planetarium Park, on Eighty-first Street in New York City. The bird was never caged. It was free to come and go. At will, it flew in and out of the apartment window more than 130 feet above the street.

On rainy days, the sparrow made no effort to mount upward along the sheer cliff of brick and glass to Bennett's apartment window. Instead, she rode up on the elevator! Flying in the front entrance of the apartment house, Snobber alighted on the shoulder of the elevator operator, Frank Olmedo. When they reached the eleventh floor, Olmedo rang the bell at the apartment. And when the door opened, the sparrow flew, like a homing pigeon, to the boy's bedroom. One summer during a month when Bennett was away at a summer camp, Olmedo cared for the bird, and the two became fast friends.

Bennett had found Snobber in Central Park when the bird was just a baby. He carried it home and installed it in an empty robin's nest in his room. With the aid of a medicine dropper and a pair of tweezers, he fed it at hourly intervals. On a diet of flies, bits of worms, water, and pieces of egg-biscuit, it grew rapidly. It gained weight, and the whitish fuzz on its body developed into scores of strong, glossy feathers. A snobbish tilt of the beak when the sparrow had eaten enough gave it its name.

The boy taught Snobber to fly by placing her in low trees, offering food, and chirping to her. The sparrow learned to recognize his chirp and would fly up to the apartment window from the trees below when Bennett called. To the uninitiated all sparrows seem to chirp alike. But not to Bennett. He could recognize Snobber's chirp in a tree full of sparrows. By the sound, he could tell whether she was angry, curious, or excited. When they went outside together, they often seemed to be carrying on a conversation, chirping back and forth, as the sparrow darted ahead from tree to tree. On reaching Eighty-first Street, Snobber flew on ahead and waited at the entrance of the apartment house for Bennett to cross the street.

A friendly bird, she often was much in evidence when the boys of the neighborhood were playing games. In the middle of a baseball game, she sometimes alighted on the shoulders of the batter or settled down directly on the base line to attract attention. At other times, when the boys were flipping their card collection of baseball players, Snobber would dart down, grasp one of the cards in her bill, and fly away with it. Any small, shiny object instantly aroused her interest. When she found a dime on Bennett's dresser, she picked it up and darted this way and that,

---

uninitiated—*inexperienced*

flying until she tired. Two marbles in a small metal tray on the boy's desk kept her occupied for a quarter of an hour at a time. She pushed them about with her bill, apparently delighted by the jangling sound they made.

Along Eighty-first Street, pedestrians were often as surprised as were the people of Vineland to have a sparrow swoop down and alight on their shoulders. The reaction was varied. One woman took off a fur neckpiece and swung it around in the air like a lasso to ward off the supposed attack. Several persons made a grab for the sparrow. But Snobber always was too quick for them.

One summer day, a nearsighted gentleman, wearing a derby hat, was walking down the Planetarium side of Eighty-first Street reading a newspaper held close to his face. In his left hand he clutched an ice-cream cone from which he absentmindedly took a bite from time to time. Snobber was perched on the lower limb of a tree. She cocked her head as he went by; she had sighted the ice cream. Swooping down, she alighted on the cone and began nibbling away. Just then the man put the cone to his mouth abstractedly to take another bite. The cone bit him, instead! Or, at least, that was the impression he got when Snobber pecked him on the lower lip. Unable to believe his eyes, he peered nearsightedly at the cone and bird. Then he began to wave the cone in circles in the air. Like a pinwheel, the cone and the pursuing sparrow whirled above his head.

Seeing the commotion, Bennett ran across the street to explain and to catch Snobber. But in the process he accidently knocked the cone from the man's hand. Thinking he was being set upon from the air and the ground simultaneously, the near-sighted gentleman clutched his newspaper in one hand and his derby hat in the other and sprinted, puffing, down the street. At the end of the block, he stopped, turned, shook his fist, and hurried around the corner.

Indoors, when Snobber got hungry she perched on a seed box as a signal to the boy. Two of her favorite foods, aside from seeds and bits of biscuit, were cornflakes and maple sugar. She got greens by eating pieces of leaves from time to time. If the sash was down when she wanted to fly out the window, she dashed about the room in a special manner that Bennett learned to understand.

As might be supposed, the sparrow, when outside, had difficulty at first picking out the right window among the vast number that pierced the masonry of the great apartment house. Once, after Bennett had chirped to her with his head out the window, he was called back into the room. When he looked out again, he was just in time to see the sparrow come flying out of a window on the floor below. As a guide for Snobber he tied a ribbon on the iron bar of a window box outside his bedroom. Before dusk, Snobber always returned to the apartment. The only time she spent the night outdoors was during the days when she was lost near Vineland.

From the beginning, Bennett determined that if Snobber ever wanted to go free he would not try to restrain her. The train trip to Vineland, that first summer, was one of the few times when she had been locked in a cage. The ride was bumpy, and she disliked it, chirping most of the time. Bennett spent his time during the journey explaining to interested passengers about the sparrow in the cage. At his uncle's farm, Snobber was ill at ease. She had never seen a rocking chair before, and the unstable perch it provided when the boy was sitting in it disturbed her still more.

sash—*window frame*

104

On the second day at the farm, she dashed from an apple tree in pursuit of two sparrows, flew too far, became confused, then hopelessly lost. Four days later, when Bennett recovered her through his advertisement, she was several miles from his uncle's farm in the direction of New York City. She recognized the boy in an instant and flew chirping to his shoulder. A small American flag in the window of the house where she was found resembled the ribbon tied to the window box of the apartment house and may have influenced her in choosing that particular place.

Her first spring, Snobber built a nest. Tearing up a robin's and a song sparrow's nest that Bennett had in his room, she used the material to create a nest of her own.

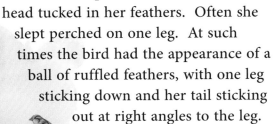

English Sparrow Egg Laid by Snobber

She was busy with this task for days, sometimes flying about the room with straws fully a foot long. In the nest she laid two eggs. Neither hatched, and one later rested on cotton batting in a small box in Bennett's room. The box bore on the lid the notation: English Sparrow Egg Laid by Snobber.

When Bennett was doing his homework, during the winter, Snobber often perched quietly on his book or on the desk beside him. And at night, when the boy was sleeping in his bed, the sparrow was lost in slumber on the top of the closet door, her head tucked in her feathers. Often she slept perched on one leg. At such times the bird had the appearance of a ball of ruffled feathers, with one leg sticking down and her tail sticking out at right angles to the leg.

As soon as it was daylight, Snobber awoke. Bennett didn't need an alarm clock. He had Snobber.

She hopped down, perched on his head, and began tugging at individual hairs. If he didn't wake up, she often snuggled down near his neck for an additional nap herself. If he disturbed her by moving in his sleep, she pecked him on the chest. As a consequence, Bennett often kept moving back toward the far side of the bed until, when he awakened, he was lying on the edge and the sparrow was occupying most of the bed.

Like Mary's famous little lamb, Snobber sometimes tried to follow Bennett to school. He rode to and from classes on the subway. Winter mornings, he always tried to leave the apartment house without the sparrow seeing him. But the bright eyes of the little bird missed little that was going on. Several times, just as he was sprinting a block from his home, he heard a lively chirping behind him and Snobber fluttered down on his shoulder. Twice he had to explain to teachers that he was late for classes because a sparrow had delayed him! At the school he attended, however, both teachers and pupils knew all about Snobber. In fact, whenever Bennett got an extra good grade, his classmates had a standing explanation: *Snobber had helped him!*

Character Theme—Friendship

Time to Think

1. What kind of bird was Snobber?
2. How did Snobber and Bennett get to be friends?
3. What were some of Snobber's unusual habits?
4. Where did Snobber sleep?
5. Why did Bennett tie a ribbon on the window box outside his bedroom window?

*Associate with men of good quality
if you esteem your own reputation, for it is better
to be alone than in bad company.*
—George Washington

Companions

Margaret Slattery

Companions whom one has deliberately chosen may make or mar character. Those of whom we approve, with whom we choose to live in intimate, daily friendship, are one of the determining factors in our lives. If one chooses to remain in close companionship with the vulgar and mean he cannot keep himself pure in heart. He will listen to things that besmirch—at first will listen, resenting what he hears, then as the days pass, accepting it, and after a while repeating it. If the proposals of his companions for good times and a lark at first meet with disapproval, then with a reluctant consent, and he continues to remain with them, the reluctance will slowly change to a willing consent. Finally he will propose larks of the same sort or worse, himself. This is the law. We become like the thing with which we choose habitually to associate.

If you find that you are critical, fault-finding, continually complaining of your work and your lot in life; if you use a great deal of slang, are accused of being rude in speech and in manner, note your companions; in nine cases out of ten you will find that these are their faults also.

If our companions are purer, finer, more noble than we, though at first we may follow them afar off, yet if we choose to continue the close association until the companionship ripens into friendship, we shall slowly grow like them. That also is the law.

---

mar—*damage*
besmirch—*defile; make unclean*

lark—*a time of adventure, jokes,
and pranks*

As soon as we are old enough to desire close companions, we may choose them, and upon our choice depends in large measure our future. William Gladstone felt that so much depends upon the choice of compan-

ions that, looking into the faces of hundreds of young men who had asked him to give them some advice, he said, "Choose wisely your companions, for a young man's companions, more than his food, his clothes, his home or his parents, make him what he is."

If you are wise, you will spend much time and thought in choosing those who are to be your friends. Do not choose them for what they wear, do not choose them because of the place in which they live, never choose them because they may be useful to you socially or in business. Choose them for what they are. Choose them because they are good, fine, honest, worthwhile, and constant association with them will make you a better young man or woman.

William Gladstone—*a British prime minister in the 1800s*

Character Theme—Friendship & Wisdom

Time to Think

1. What is the law of friendships?
2. On what basis should we choose our friends?

The Art of Friendship

Wilferd A. Peterson

The first step in the art of friendship is to be a friend; then making friends takes care of itself. To be a friend a man should start by being a friend to himself, by being true to his highest and best and by aligning himself with the enduring values of human life that make for growth and progress.

To be a friend a man should strive to be "like the shadow of a great rock in a weary land," to be a source of refuge and strength to those who walk in darkness.

To be a friend a man should strive to lift people up, not cast them down; to encourage, not discourage; to set an example that will be an inspiration to others.

To be a friend a man should be sensitively responsive to the dreams and aims of others and should show sincere appreciation for the contributions others make to the enrichment of his life.

To be a friend a man should practice the companionship of silence and the magic of words that his speech may build and not destroy, help and not hinder.

To be a friend a man should be himself, he should be done with hypocrisy, artificiality and pretense, he should meet and mingle with people in quiet simplicity and humility.

To be a friend a man should be tolerant, he should have an understanding heart and a forgiving nature, knowing that all men stumble now and then, and that he who never made a mistake never accomplished anything.

To be a friend a man should go more than halfway with his fellow men; he should greet others first and not wait to be greeted; he should radiate a spirit of overflowing good will.

To be a friend a man should remember that we are human magnets; that like attracts like, and that what we give we get.

To be a friend a man should recognize that no man knows all the answers, and that he should add each day to his knowledge of how to live the friendly way.

---

radiate—*to send forth on all sides*

Character Theme—Friendship & Integrity

Time to Think

1. Did you learn some ways in which you can be a better friend? What are some ways you can encourage friends?
2. How can we avoid being hypocritical and artificial in our friendships?

I expect to pass through this life but once.
If there is any kindness or any good thing I can do
let me do it now: I shall pass this way but once.

Jo's Sacrifice

Louisa May Alcott

MEET THE AUTHOR

Louisa May Alcott wrote *Little Women,* one of America's best-loved stories. The book was so popular that readers wanted to hear more about Meg, Jo, Beth, and Amy March, the "four little women," who were really Louisa May and her sisters.

She soon wrote *Little Men, Jo's Boys, Eight Cousins,* and other stories. This story is from *Little Women.*

Louisa May Alcott lived from 1832–1888 and lived most of her life around Boston.

Mrs. March:

Your husband is very ill. Come at once.

    S. Hale

    Blank Hospital, Washington.

How still the room was as they listened breathlessly, and how suddenly the whole world seemed to change, as the girls gathered about their mother. Mrs. March read the message over, and in a tone they never forgot said, "I shall go at once, but it may be too late." Then turning to Laurie, she said, "Leave a note at Aunt March's. Jo, give me the pen and paper."

Jo drew the table before her mother, well knowing the money for the long, sad journey must be borrowed, and feeling as if she could do anything to add a little to the sum for her father. Then she went out to buy several articles her mother needed for the journey.

The short afternoon wore away, but Jo did not return. They began to get anxious, and Laurie went off to find her. He missed her, however, and she came walking in with a very queer expression of countenance, for there was a mixture of fun and fear, satisfaction and regret, in it, which puzzled the family as much as did the roll of bills she laid before her mother, saying, with a little choke in her voice, "That's my contribution towards making Father comfortable and bringing him home!"

"My dear, where did you get it? Twenty-five dollars! Jo, I hope you haven't done anything rash."

"No, it's mine honestly; I didn't beg, borrow, or steal it. I earned it; and I don't think you'll blame me, for I only sold what was my own."

As she spoke, Jo took off her bonnet, and a general outcry arose, for all her abundant hair was cut short.

"Your hair! Your beautiful hair!"

"O Jo, how could you? Your one beauty."

"My dear girl, there was no need of this."

"She doesn't look like my Jo any more, but I love her dearly for it!"

As everyone exclaimed, and Beth hugged the cropped head tenderly, Jo assumed an indifferent air, which did not deceive anyone a particle, and said, rumpling up the brown bush, and trying to look as if she liked it: "It doesn't affect the fate of the nation, so don't wail, Beth. It will be good for my vanity; I was getting too proud of my wig. It will do my brains good to have that mop taken off; my head feels deliciously light and cool, and the barber said I could soon have a curly crop, which will be boyish, becoming, and easy to keep in order. I'm satisfied; so please take the money, and let's have supper."

"What made you do it?" asked Amy, who would as soon have thought of cutting off her head as her pretty hair.

---

rash—*bold and hasty*

112

"Well, I was wild to do something for Father," replied Jo, as they gathered about the table, for healthy young people can eat even in the midst of trouble. "I hate to borrow as much as Mother does, and I knew Aunt March would croak; she always does, if you ask for a ninepence. Meg gave all her quarterly salary toward the rent, and I only got some clothes with mine, so I felt wicked, and was bound to have some money, if I sold the nose off my face to get it."

"You needn't feel wicked, my child: You had no winter things, and got the simplest with your own hard earnings," said Mrs. March, with a look that warmed Jo's heart.

"I hadn't the least idea of selling my hair at first, but as I went along, I kept thinking what I could do. In a barber's window I saw tails of hair with the prices marked; and one black tail, not so thick as mine, was forty dollars. It came over me all of a sudden that I had one thing to make money out of, and without stopping to think, I walked in, asked if they bought hair, and what they would give for mine."

"I don't see how you dared to do it," said Beth, in a tone of awe.

"Oh, he was a little man who looked as if he merely lived to oil his hair. He rather stared, at first, as if he wasn't used to having girls bounce into his shop and ask him to buy their hair. He said he didn't care about mine, it wasn't the fashionable color, and he never paid much for it in the first place; the work put into it made it dear, and so on. It was getting late and I was afraid, if it wasn't done right away that I shouldn't have it done at all, and you know when I start to do a thing, I hate to give it up; so I begged him to take it, and told him why I was in such a hurry. It was silly, I dare say, but it changed his mind, for I got rather excited, and told the story in my topsy-turvy way, and his wife heard, and said so kindly,—

ninepence—*a silver coin worth about nine pennies*

" 'Take it, Thomas, and oblige the young lady; I'd do as much for our Jimmy any day if I had a spire of hair worth selling.' "

"Who was Jimmy?" asked Amy, who liked to have things explained as they went along.

"Her son, she said, who was in the army. How friendly such things make strangers feel, don't they? She talked away all the time the man clipped, and diverted my mind nicely."

"Didn't you feel dreadfully when the first cut came?" asked Meg, with a shiver.

"I took a last look at my hair while the man got his things, and that was the end of it. I never snivel over trifles like that; I will confess, though, I felt strange when I saw the dear old hair laid out on the table, and felt only the short rough ends on my head. It almost seemed as if I'd an arm or a leg off. The woman saw me look at it, and picked out a long lock for me to keep.

---

spire—*a mound of curls*   snivel—*whine or complain*

I'll give it to you, Marmee, just to remember past glories by; for a crop is so comfortable I don't think I shall ever have a mane again."

Mrs. March folded the wavy chestnut lock, and laid it away with a short gray one in her desk. She only said, "Thank you, deary," but something in her face made the girls change the subject, and talk as cheerfully as they could about the prospect of a fine day tomorrow, and the happy times they would have when father came home to be nursed.

No one wanted to go to bed, when at ten o'clock Mrs. March put by the last finished job, and said, "Come, girls." Beth went to the piano and played the father's favorite hymn; all began bravely, but broke down one by one, till Beth was left alone, singing with all her heart, for to her music was always a sweet consoler.

"Go to bed and don't talk, for we must be up early, and shall need all the sleep we can get. Good night, my darlings," said Mrs. March, as the hymn ended, for no one cared to try another.

They kissed her quietly, and went to bed as silently as if the dear invalid lay in the next room. Beth and Amy soon fell asleep in spite of the great trouble. Jo lay motionless, and Meg fancied that she was asleep, till a stifled sob made her exclaim, as she touched a wet cheek,—

"Jo, dear, what is it? Are you crying about Father?"

"No, not now."

"What, then?"

"My—my hair!" burst out poor Jo, trying vainly to smother her emotion in the pillow.

"I'm not sorry," she protested, with a choke. "I'd do it again tomorrow, if I could. It's only the vain, selfish part of me that goes and cries in this silly way. Don't tell any one, it's all over now. I thought you asleep, so I just made a little private moan for my one beauty. And now for sleep."

The clocks were striking midnight, and the rooms were very still, as a figure glided quietly from bed to bed, smoothing the coverlid here, settling a pillow there, and pausing to look long and tenderly at each unconscious face, to kiss each with lips that mutely blessed, and to pray the fervent prayers which only mothers utter. As she lifted the curtain to look out into the dreary night, the moon broke suddenly from behind the clouds, and shone upon her like a bright, benignant face, which seemed to whisper in the silence: "Be comforted, dear soul! There is always light behind the clouds."

benignant—*kind*

Character Theme—Sacrifice & Resourcefulness

Time to Think

1. What was Jo's sacrifice?
2. Why did the family need money?
3. How did Jo feel about her sacrifice?
4. What sacrifice could you make to help someone you know?
5. Describe Jo.

Our History
Catherine Cate Coblentz

Our history sings of centuries
Such varying songs it sings!
It starts with winds, slow moving sails.
It ends with skies and wings.

America for Me

Henry van Dyke

'Tis fine to see the Old World, and travel up and down
Among the famous palaces and cities of renown,
To admire the crumbly castles and the statues of the kings—
But now I think I've had enough of antiquated things.

So it's home again, and home again, America for me!
My heart is turning home again, and there I long to be,
In the land of youth and freedom beyond the ocean bars,
Where the air is full of sunlight and the flag is full of stars.

Oh, London is a man's town; there's power in the air;
And Paris is a woman's town, with flowers in her hair;
And it's sweet to dream in Venice, and it's great to study Rome;
But when it comes to living, there is no place like home.

I like the German fir-woods, in green battalions drilled;
I like the gardens of Versailles, with flashing fountains filled;
But, oh, to take your hand, my dear, and ramble for a day
In the friendly western woodland, where nature has her way!

I know that Europe's wonderful, yet something seems to lack;
The past is too much with her, and the people looking back.
But the glory of the present is to make the future free—
We love our land for what she is, and what she is to be.

Oh, it's home again, and home again, America for me!
I want a ship that's westward bound to plow the rolling sea
To the blessed Land of Room Enough beyond the ocean bars,
Where the air is full of sunlight and the flag is full of stars.

---

renown—*great fame*   **antiquated**—*very old*   **Versailles** (vər·sī′)

In the United States we believe in the worth of every individual. Weary, oppressed hearts all over the world look longingly to America as the land of hope. Many, like Ivan, dream of one day coming to America to live, to work, and to enjoy the priceless blessings of liberty.

The Citizen

James Francis Dwyer

About a year after the beginning of World War I two thousand foreigners who had recently been naturalized were welcomed to American citizenship at a great gathering in Philadelphia. The times were critical; submarine warfare with all its cruelty had recently been begun; three days before, the passenger ship *Lusitania* had been sunk with a loss of 112 Americans; many people felt that the loyalty of all Americans, both the native-born and foreign-born, would soon be severely tested. Several thousand men and women listened intently to the chief address on this occasion, given by President Woodrow Wilson. Stirred by the dramatic nature of the event, Mr. Dwyer, himself a naturalized American, wrote this story.

The President of the United States was speaking. His audience comprised two thousand foreign-born men who had just been admitted to citizenship. They listened intently, their faces aglow with the light of a newborn patriotism, upturned to the calm, intellectual face of the first citizen of the country they now claimed as their own.

Here and there among the newly made citizens were wives and children. The women were proud of their men. They looked at their husbands from time to time, their faces showing admiration and awe.

One little woman, sitting immediately in front of the President, held the hand of a big muscular man and stroked it softly. The man was looking at the speaker with great blue eyes that were the eyes of a dreamer.

---

naturalized—*admitted to citizenship*   comprised—*included*

The President's words came clear and distinct:

"You were drawn across the ocean by some beckoning finger of hope, by some belief of a new kind of justice, by some expectation of a better kind of life. You dreamed dreams of this country, and I hope you brought the dreams with you. A man enriches the country to which he brings dreams, and you who have brought them have enriched America."

The big man made a curious choking noise and his wife breathed a soft "Hush!" The giant was strangely affected.

The President continued:

"No doubt you have been disappointed in some of us; but remember this: if we have grown at all poor in the ideal, you brought some of it with you. A man does not go out to seek the thing that is not in him. A man does not hope for the thing that he does not believe in, and if some of us have forgotten what America believed in, you at any rate imported in your own hearts a renewal of the belief. Each of you, I am sure, brought a dream, a glorious, shining dream, a dream worth more than gold or silver, and that is the reason that I, for one, make you welcome."

The big man's eyes were fixed. His wife shook him gently, but he did not heed her. He was looking past the speaker's platform, through the big buildings behind it, looking out over leagues of space to a snow-swept village on an island in the Beresina, the swift-flowing tributary of the mighty Dnieper, an island that looked like a back bone stuck tight in the maw of the stream.

* * *

It was in the little village on the Beresina that the Dream came to Ivan Berloff.

The Dream came in the spring. All great dreams come in the spring, and the Spring Maiden who brought Big Ivan's Dream was more than ordinarily beautiful. She swept up the Beresina, trailing wondrous draperies of vivid green. Her feet touched the snow-hardened ground, and armies of little white and blue flowers sprang up in her footsteps.

The father of Big Ivan, who had fought under Prince Menshikov fifty-five years before, hobbled out to see the sunbeams eat up the snow that hid in the shady places.

"The little breezes are hot and sweet," he said, sniffing hungrily, with his face turned toward the south. "They have the spice odor that I sniffed on the winds that came to us when we soldiers lay in the trenches. Praise God for the warmth."

And that day the Dream came to Big Ivan as he plowed. Like his father, he sniffed the sweet-smelling breezes. He reached down and plucked one of a bunch of white flowers that had sprung up overnight. The Dream was born of the breezes and the sunshine and the spring flowers.

That evening Big Ivan spoke to his wife, Anna, a little woman who had a sweet face and a wealth of fair hair.

---

leagues—*units of distance equal to three miles each*
Dnieper (nē′pər)

maw—*the mouth of a stream*
Menshikov (mĕn′chĭ·kôv)

"Wife, we are going away from here," he said.

"Where are we going, Ivan?" she asked.

"Where do you think, Anna?" he said, looking down at her as she stood by his side.

"To Bobruisk," she murmured.

"No."

"Farther?"

"Aye, a long way farther."

Fear sprang into her soft eyes. Bobruisk was eighty-nine versts away, yet Ivan said they were going farther.

"We—we are not going to Minsk?" she cried.

"Aye, and beyond Minsk!"

"Ivan, tell me!" she gasped. "Tell me where we are going!"

"We are going to America."

"To America!"

"Yes, to America!"

Big Ivan lifted up his voice when he cried out the words "To America," and then a sudden fear sprang upon him as those words dashed through the little window out into the darkness of the village street. Was he mad? America was eight thousand versts away! It was far across the ocean, a place where he knew no one.

Anna remained staring at her big husband for a few minutes; then she sat down quietly at his side. There was a strange look in his big, blue eyes—the look of a man to whom has come a vision, the look which came into the eyes of those shepherds of Judea long, long ago.

"What is it, Ivan?" she murmured softly, patting his big hand. "Tell me."

And Big Ivan, slow of tongue, told of the Dream. To no one else would he have told it. Anna understood. She had a way of patting his hands and saying soft things when his tongue could not find words to express his thoughts.

Bobruisk (bŭ·brōō′ĭsk)

verst—*a Russian measure of distance equal to a little more than half a mile*

Ivan told how the Dream had come to him as he plowed. He told her how it had sprung upon him, a dream born of the soft breezes, of the sunshine, of the sweet smell of the upturned sod, and of his own strength. "It wouldn't come to weak men," he said, baring an arm that showed great muscles rippling beneath the clear skin. "It is a dream that comes only to those who are strong and those who want—who want something that they haven't got." Then in a lower voice he said, "What is it that we want, Anna?"

The little wife looked out into the darkness with fear-filled eyes. There were spies in that little village of the Beresina, and it was dangerous to say words that might be regarded as a reflection on the government. But she answered Ivan. She stopped and whispered one word into his ear, and he slapped his thigh with his big hand.

"Aye," he cried, "that is what we want! You and I and millions like us want it, and over there, Anna, over there we shall get it."

Anna stood up, took a small jar from a side shelf, dusted it carefully, and placed it upon the mantel. From a knotted cloth about her neck she took a ruble and dropped the coin into the jar. Big Ivan looked at her curiously. "It is to make legs for your Dream," she explained. "It is many versts to America, and one rides on rubles."

"You are a good wife," he said. "I was afraid you might laugh at me."

"It is a great dream," she murmured.

The Dream maddened Ivan during the days that followed. He wanted to be moving, but Anna had said that one rode on rubles, and rubles were hard to find.

In some mysterious way the village became aware of the secret. Donkov the tailor discovered it. Donkov lived in one-

---

ruble—*a Russian coin*

half of the cottage occupied by Ivan and Anna, and he had long ears. The tailor spread the news, and Poborino the smith and Yanansk the baker would jeer at Ivan as he passed.

"When are you going to America?" they would ask.

"Soon," Ivan would answer.

"Take us with you!" they would cry in chorus.

"It is no place for cowards," Ivan would answer. "It is a long way, and only brave men can make the journey."

"Are you brave?" the baker screamed one day as Ivan went by.

"I am brave enough to want liberty!" cried Ivan, angrily, "I am brave enough to want—"

"Be careful! Be careful!" interrupted the smith. "A long tongue has given many a man a train journey that he never expected."

That night Ivan and Anna counted the rubles in the earthenware pot. The giant looked down at his wife with a gloomy face, but she smiled and patted his hand.

"It is slow work," he said.

"We must be patient," she answered. "You have the Dream."

"Aye," he said, "I have the Dream."

Through the hot summertime the Dream grew within the brain of Big Ivan. At times he would stand, hoe in hand, and look towards the west, the wonderful west into which the sun slipped down each evening just like a coin dropped from the fingers of the dying day.

Autumn came, and the fretful whining winds from the north chilled the Dream. The winds whispered of the coming of the Snow King, and the river grumbled as it listened. Autumn is a bad time for dreams.

Winter came and the Dream weakened. It was only the earthenware pot that kept it alive, the pot into which the industrious Anna put every coin that could be spared.

"You are a good woman, Anna," Ivan would say again and again. "It was you who thought of saving the rubles."

"But it was you who dreamed," she would answer. "Wait for the spring, husband mine. Wait."

It was strange how the spring came to the Beresina that year. It swept the river, escorted by a million little breezes, and housewives opened their windows and peered out with surprise upon their faces.

Big Ivan was fixing a fence in the meadow on the morning the Spring Maiden reached the village. His mind was upon his work, but suddenly he discovered that he was hot, and he took off his coat. He turned to hang the coat upon a bush; then he sniffed the air. He sniffed again, hurriedly, hungrily. It was wonderful air. It brought life to the Dream. It rose up within him ten times more powerful than on the day it was born.

Big Ivan clutched his coat and ran to the little cottage. He burst through the door, startling Anna, who was busy with her housework.

"The Spring!" he cried. "The Spring!"

He took her arm and dragged her to the door. In silence they listened to the song of the river. Anna pointed to a green bud on a bush beside the door.

"It came this minute," she murmured.

Together they turned and walked to the mantle. Big Ivan took up the earthenware pot, carried it to the table, and spilled its contents upon the well-scrubbed boards. He counted while Anna stood beside him, her fingers clutching his coarse blouse. It was slow business, because Ivan's big blunt fingers were not used to such work, but it was over at last.

"It is enough," he said quietly. "We will go at once. If it was not enough we would have to go because the Dream is upon me, and I hate this place."

"As you say," murmured Anna. "The wife of the butcher will buy our chairs and our bed. I spoke to her yesterday."

Poborino the smith, Yanansk the baker, Donkov the tailor, and a score of others were out upon the village street on the

morning that Big Ivan and Anna set out. They were inclined to
jeer at Ivan, but something upon the face of the giant made them
afraid. Hand in hand the big man and his wife walked down the
street, Ivan balancing upon his head a heavy trunk that no other
man in the village could have lifted.

At the end of the street a boy with bright eyes and yellow
curls clutched the hand of Ivan and looked into his face.

"I know what is sending you," he cried.

"Aye, *you* know," said Ivan, looking into the eyes of the
other.

"It came to me yesterday," murmured the lad. "I got it from
the breezes. They are free; so are the birds and the little clouds
and the river. I wish I could go."

"Keep your dream," said Ivan softly. "Nurse it, for it is the
dream of a man."

Anna, who was crying softly, touched the blouse of the boy.

126

"At the back of our cottage, near the bush that bears the red berries, a pot is buried," she said. "Dig it up and take it home with you, and when you have a kopek drop it in. It is a good pot."

The stripling understood. He stopped and kissed the hand of Anna, and Big Ivan patted him upon the back. They were brother dreamers and they understood each other.

Big Ivan and Anna faced the long versts to Bobruisk, but they were not afraid. They had the Dream. America was a long, long journey, but they had started, and every verst they covered lessened the number that lay between them and the Promised Land.

"I am glad the boy spoke to us," said Anna.

"And I am glad," said Ivan. "Some day he will come and eat with us in America."

They came to Bobruisk. Holding hands, they walked into it late one afternoon. They were eighty-nine versts from the little village of Beresina, but they were not afraid. The railway ran through Bobruisk and that evening they stood and looked at the shining rails that went out in the moonlight like silver tongs reaching out for a low-hanging star.

They came face to face with the Terror that evening, the Terror that had helped the spring breezes and the sunshine to plant the Dream in the brain of Big Ivan.

They were walking down a dark street when they saw a score of men and women creep from the door of an unpainted building. The little group remained on the sidewalk for a minute as if uncertain about the way they should go; then came a cry of "Police!"

It was no false alarm. Mounted police charged down the dark thoroughfare swinging their swords at the scurrying men and women who raced for shelter. Big Ivan dragged Anna into

---

kopek—*a Russian coin*   stripling—*young person*

a doorway, and toward their hiding place ran a young boy who, like themselves, had no connection with the group and who merely desired to get out of harm's way.

The boy was not quick enough to escape the charge. A trooper pursued him, overtook him before he reached the sidewalk, and knocked him down with the flat of his sword. His horse struck the boy with one of his hoofs as the lad stumbled and fell.

Big Ivan growled like an angry bear and sprang from his hiding place. The trooper's horse had carried him onto the sidewalk, and Ivan seized the bridle and flung the animal on its haunches. The policeman leaned forward to strike at the giant, but Ivan gripped the left leg of the horseman and tore him from his saddle.

The horse galloped off, leaving its rider lying beside the moaning boy who was unlucky enough to be in a street where a score of students were holding a meeting.

Anna dragged Ivan back into the passageway. More police were charging down the street and their position was dangerous.

"Ivan!" she cried, "Ivan! Remember the Dream! America! Ivan! America! Come this way! Quick!"

With strong hands she dragged him down the passage. They hurried toward the place where they had taken lodging. From far off came screams and hoarse orders, curses, and the sound of galloping hoofs. The Terror was abroad.

Big Ivan spoke softly as he entered the little room they had taken. "He had a face like the boy to whom you gave the lucky pot," he said. "Did you notice it in the moonlight when the trooper struck him down?"

"Yes," she answered, "I saw."

They left Bobruisk next morning. They rode away on a great puffing, snorting train that terrified Anna. The real journey had begun. They began to love the powerful engine. It was eating up the versts at a tremendous rate.

They came to Minsk, the biggest town they had ever seen. They looked out from the car windows at the miles of wooden buildings, at the big church, and the woolen mills.

On and on went the train, the wheels singing the song of the road. Fellow travelers asked them where they were going. "To America," Ivan would answer.

"To America!" they would cry. "May God guide you! It is a long way, and you will be lonely."

"No, we shall not be lonely," Ivan would say.

"Ha! You are going with friends?"

"No, we have no friends, but we have something that keeps us from being lonely." And when Ivan would make that reply Anna would pat his hand and the questioner would wonder if it was a charm or a holy relic that the bright-eyed couple possessed.

They ran through Vilna, on through flat stretches of Courland to Libau, where they first saw the sea. They sat and stared at it for a whole day, talking little but watching it with wide, wondering eyes.

The harbor master spoke to Ivan and Anna as they watched the restless waters.

"Where are you going, children?"

"To America," answered Ivan.

"A long way. Three ships bound for America went down last month."

"Ours will not sink," said Ivan.

"Why?"

"Because I know it will not."

The harbor master looked at the strange blue eyes of the giant and spoke softly. "You have the eyes of a man who sees things," he said. "There was a Norwegian sailor in the *White Queen* with eyes like yours and he could see death."

Courland (kŏōr'lənd)

"I see life!" said Ivan, boldly. "A free life—"

"Hush!" said the harbor master. "Do not speak so loud." He walked swiftly away, but he dropped a ruble into Anna's hand as he passed her by. "For luck," he murmured. "May God look after you on the big waters."

They boarded the ship, and the Dream gave them a courage that surprised them. There were others going abroad, and Ivan and Anna felt that the others were also persons who possessed dreams. Anna saw the dreams in their eyes. There were Slavs, Poles, Letts, Jews, and Livonians, all bound for the land where dreams come true.

The emigrant ship was dragged from her pier by a grunting tug and went floundering down the Baltic Sea. Night came down and a storm attacked the ship and tried to stand her on her head. Anna lay sick in the stuffy women's quarters, and Ivan could not get near her. But he sent her messages. He told her not to mind the storm, to think of the Dream.

Ivan grew to full stature on that first night out from Libau. He was not afraid. Down amid the smells of the steerage he induced a thin-faced Livonian to play upon a mouth organ, and Big Ivan sang Paleer's "Song of Freedom" in a voice that drowned the creaking of the old vessel's timbers and made the seasick ones forget their sickness. They sat up in their berths and joined in the chorus, their eyes shining brightly in the half gloom:

> "Freedom for serf and for slave,
> Freedom for all men who crave
> Their right to be free
> And who hate to bend knee
> But to Him who this right to them gave."

Slavs—*Slavic-speaking people from Eastern Europe*

Poles—*people from Poland*

Letts—*people from Latvia, a country of northern Europe*

Livonians—*people from Livonia, a region of northern Europe*

steerage—*the least expensive rooms on a ship*

130

The emigrant ship pounded the Cattegat, swung southward through the Skagerrack and the bleak North Sea. But the storm pursued her. The big waves snarled at her, and the captain and the chief officer consulted with each other. They decided to run into the Thames, and the harried steamer nosed her way in and anchored off Gravesend.

An examination was made, and the agents decided to transship the emigrants. They were taken to London and thence by train to Liverpool. Ivan and Anna sat again side by side, holding hands and smiling at each other.

"You are not afraid?" Ivan would say to her each time she looked at him.

"It is a long way, but the Dream has given me courage," she said.

"Today I spoke to a Lett whose brother works in New York City," said the Giant. "Do you know how much money he earns each day?"

"How much?" she questioned.

"Three rubles—and he calls the policemen by their first names."

"You will earn five rubles, my Ivan," she murmured. "There is no one as strong as you."

Once again they were herded into a big ship that steamed away through the fog banks out into the Irish Sea.

The Atlantic was kind. Through sunny days Ivan and Anna sat up on deck and watched the horizon. They wanted to be among those who would get the first glimpse of the wonderland.

They saw it on a morning with sunshine and soft winds. Standing together in the bow, they looked at the smear upon the horizon and their eyes filled with tears. They forgot the long road to Bobruisk, the rocking journey to Libau, the storm of the

---

Cattegat (kăt′ĭ·găt′)
Skagerrack (skăg′ə·răk′)

transship—*to transfer from one ship to another*

131

Baltic. Everything unpleasant was forgotten because the Dream filled them with a great happiness.

The inspectors at Ellis Island were interested in Ivan. They walked around him and prodded his muscles, and Ivan smiled down upon them good-naturedly.

"A fine animal," said one. "He's a new white hope! Ask him if he can fight."

An interpreter put the question, and Ivan nodded. "I have fought," he said.

"Ask him was it for purses or what," cried the inspector.

"For freedom," answered Ivan.

Ivan and Anna left the government ferryboat at the Battery. They started to walk uptown, Ivan carrying the big trunk that no other man could lift.

It was a wonderful morning. The city was bathed in warm sunshine, and the well-dressed men and women who crowded the sidewalks made the two immigrants think that it was a holiday. Ivan and Anna stared at each other in amazement.

"It is a feast day for certain," said Anna.

"They are dressed like princes and princesses," murmured Ivan. "There are no poor here, Anna. None."

Like two simple children they walked along the streets of the City of Wonder. What a contrast it was to the gray towns where the Terror awaited to spring upon the people.

They lost their way, but they walked on, looking at the shop windows, the elevated trains, and the huge skyscrapers. Hours afterward they found themselves in Fifth Avenue near Thirty-third Street, and there a miracle happened to them—a big miracle because it proved the Dream a truth, a great truth.

Ivan and Anna attempted to cross the avenue, but they became confused in the traffic. Anna screamed, and in response to her scream a traffic policeman, resplendent in a new uniform, rushed to her side. The charging autos halted; for five blocks north and south they jammed on the brakes when the interruption occurred, and Big Ivan gasped.

resplendent—*brilliant*

"Don't be flurried, little woman," said the cop. "Sure I can tame 'em by liftin' me hand."

Anna didn't understand what he said, but she knew it was something nice by the manner in which his Irish eyes smiled down upon her. And in front of the waiting automobiles he led her with the same care that he would give to a duchess, while Ivan, carrying the big trunk, followed them, wondering much. Ivan's mind went back to Bobruisk on the night the Terror was abroad.

The policeman led Anna to the sidewalk, patted Ivan on the shoulder, and then with a sharp whistle unloosed the waiting stream of cars that had been held up so that two Russian immigrants could cross the avenue.

Big Ivan took the trunk from his head and put it on the ground. He reached out his arms and folded Anna in a great embrace. His eyes were wet.

"The Dream is true!" he cried. "Did you see, Anna? This is the land where a peasant is as good as a prince of the blood."

*   *   *

The President was nearing the close of his address. Anna shook Ivan, and Ivan came out of the trance which the President's words had brought upon him. He sat up and listened intently:

"We grow great by dreams. All big men are dreamers. They see things in the soft haze of a spring day or in the red fire of a long winter's evening. Some of us let those great dreams die, but others nourish and protect them, nurse them through bad days till they bring them to the sunshine and light which come always to those who sincerely hope that their dreams will come true."

The President finished. For a moment he stood looking down at the faces turned up to him, and Big Ivan thought that the President smiled at him. Ivan seized Anna's hand and held it tight.

"He knew of my Dream!" he cried. "He knew of it. Did you hear what he said about the dreams of a spring day?"

134

"Of course he knew," said Anna. "He is the wisest man in America, where there are many wise men. Ivan, you are a citizen now."

"And you are a citizen, Anna."

The band started to play the national anthem, and Ivan and Anna got to their feet. Standing side by side, holding hands, they joined in with the others who had found after long days of journeying the blessed land where dreams come true.

Character Theme—Courage, Resolution, & Patriotism

Time to Think

1. When President Wilson welcomed the newly naturalized citizens, what special things did he say they brought to America?
2. In what country did Big Ivan and Anna live?
3. Why did Ivan dream of coming to America?
4. In what ways was Anna a good wife to Ivan?
5. Compare Ivan's native land with America.
6. Did Ivan's dream come true?

Signers of the Declaration of Independence

Frances Margaret Fox

A committee was appointed by the Continental Congress to draft the Declaration of Independence. The members of the committee were Thomas Jefferson, John Adams, Benjamin Franklin, Roger Sherman, and Robert L. R. Livingston. Jefferson and Franklin were appointed as a subcommittee to prepare the Declaration of Independence, but it fell to Jefferson to do the actual writing of the document. Only a few changes were made in this draft either by the Committee or by the Continental Congress. After Jefferson read the Declaration aloud, Franklin said, "That's good, Thomas! I wish I had done it myself." When submitted for a vote, it was adopted by the narrow margin of only one vote. The Declaration went forth signed by John Hancock, the president of the Continental Congress. As Hancock wrote his name in large, clear letters, he said, "There, John Bull can read that without spectacles, and may now double his reward of five hundred pounds for my head." Then turning, he added, "Gentlemen, we must all hang together." "Yes," replied Benjamin Franklin, "or we shall all hang separately." Later the other fifty-five members of the Continental Congress signed the document. This selection tells of the lives of these great men.

We all know that Thomas Jefferson wrote the Declaration of Independence. When he knew that he had been chosen for the honor, he ordered a desk made by a carpenter, which must have been placed on a table because it was only fourteen inches long, ten inches wide, and three inches high. On this desk he did his writing of the Declaration. Finally, when the necessary changes were made, Jefferson penned what he refers to as a "fair copy," and it was this copy which John Hancock, as President of the Congress, ordered to be engrossed on parchment, to which, at peril of their lives, the fifty-six brave men signed their names.

---

engrossed—*written as a final document*

School children who are taken to see the Declaration of Independence in the National Archives Building in Washington, D.C., are always delighted when they see John Hancock's signature; always one in the group will remind the others that John Hancock said as he wrote his name, "There, John Bull can read that without spectacles!"

John Hancock

One signature which sometimes attracts attention is the tremblingly written name of Stephen Hopkins, of Rhode Island. Those who do not know the reason for the unsteady pen often suggest that this signer surely feared the gallows. Far from it! Stephen Hopkins, ship-builder, merchant, lawyer, and colonial governor of Rhode Island, was one of the bravest men who ever lived. Usually his secretary did his writing because he was afflicted with a disease known as "shaking palsy." When he signed the Declaration, he held his right wrist with his left hand and did his best to write his name plainly. He said, "If my hand does tremble, John Bull will find that my heart won't."

Step Hopkins

137

As for Samuel Adams, when General Gage advised him to make peace with King George, this patriot firmly replied, "I trust I have long since made my peace with the King of kings. No personal considerations shall induce me to abandon the righteous cause of my country."

Sam¹ Adams

No wonder these men were long ago called "The Immortal Fifty-Six."

Josiah Bartlett

After John Hancock, Dr. Josiah Bartlett, of New Hampshire, was the next to sign the Declaration. History says he was the first to vote for it. He was one of the three "self-made men" of the fifty-six. It is a noteworthy fact that these leaders of men were, with the exception of three, all given the best education possible. Eight were Harvard graduates. Four graduated from Yale and four from Princeton. The college of William and Mary graduated three, while six were educated in England and Scotland. Several of the signers were given private tuition, "as high and costly as given at any university in the world."

Two of the signers became Presidents of the United States and two Vice-Presidents. To quote an additional bit of truth regarding the fifty-six, "Of those who survived the War for Independence, nearly every man was elected to be a senator, a congressman, a Supreme Court judge, a governor, or the President."

Of the ten who died before the close of the war, John Hart's story is the saddest. All of the signers suffered deeply "in mind, body, or estate," because of what they did for us when they signed that immortal roll; but John Hart was actually hunted for years through the swamps and woods of New Jersey by Tories who were determined upon his capture.

John Hart

The British did capture Captain Richard Stockton. They put him in jail in New York City and treated him so badly that he soon died.

Button Gwinnett is the name of a rather unusual man who arrived in our country in 1770. He was a young Englishman of great wealth who immediately joined the colonies in their struggle for freedom. At the time of the adoption of the Declaration of Independence he was in Philadelphia attending the Congress as a delegate from Georgia.

Rich. Stockton

Unfortunately the very next year he and General McIntosh had a quarrel and fought a duel in which he was mortally wounded.

Button Gwinnett

Robert Morris was also born in England, as we know. From Scotland came James Wilson and John Witherspoon. Ireland sent us James Smith, George Taylor, and Matthew Thornton, while Francis Lewis came from Wales. Here then were eight fine gentlemen straight from the realm of King George, glad to sign our Declaration of Independence.

James Wilson   Ja. Smith

Geo. Taylor   Matthew Thornton

John Witherspoon was the only clergyman numbered with the signers of the Declaration. He was fifty-four years old that July day, in 1776, so he knew what he was doing. He was a member of the War Board. They tell us that he often visited the troops and continually used his influence to make conditions easier for them. He became a college president after the war and wrote many religious books.

Jn. Witherspoon

139

Every school history tells something of the story of Robert Morris, the noble patriot who loaned his great fortune to the Continental Congress and made it possible for George Washington to compel Lord Cornwallis to surrender. For eight years Robert Morris managed the financial affairs of our country. Then when Robert Morris was an old man, at a time when our government might have saved him by paying back a little of the money which was his due, the creditors of this great man put him in a debtor's prison. No wonder he died soon!

Rob' Morris

The patriot from Wales, who was a wealthy merchant, not only lost all his property which was taken by the British, but both he and his wife were kept in prison until what King George wished to have done didn't make any particular difference in the United States of America! Francis Lewis, from Wales, was ninety years old when he died.

Fran: Lewis

When Lewis Morris signed the Declaration of Independence he well knew what was in store for him. This gentleman owned an estate of three thousand acres of the finest lands. He called his place Morrisania. There, with abundant wealth he lived like a prince. Although British troops were stationed near him and watched his every move, Lewis Morris signed the Declaration of Independence. Straightway he lost all his earthly possessions. Worst of all, his family were driven from their beautiful home as an example to all rebels. His descendants might be living at Morrisania to this day if Lewis Morris had not written his name in so conspicuous a place.

Lewis Morris

conspicuous—*noticeable*

Consider for a minute Arthur Middleton. His property also was confiscated and he suffered imprisonment which caused his death before the close of the war. Yet, as an individual who gave his all for his country, it cannot be said that his memory is sufficiently honored. Arthur Middleton was as true a patriot as John Hancock himself.

Arthur Middleton

Virginians should never forget Thomas Nelson, although to remember in detail all that befell him is far from pleasant. He saved Virginia from bankruptcy by turning his large fortune into the public treasury. At Yorktown, where he was in command of the state militia, he ordered the destruction of his own house because it seemed necessary to do so that victory might be ours.

This man, who loaned his money to the state that the soldiers of Virginia might be paid and so continue to fight the battles of the War for Independence, died at the age of fifty-one as one of the results of his generous patriotism. The remnants of his property were sold to pay his debts. When he signed the Declaration of Independence, he lost everything of value except the comfort of an approving conscience.

Tho⁵ Nelson jr.

The two Lees who signed the Declaration were wonderful men. As doubtless we all know, Francis Lightfoot Lee was one of Washington's dearest friends. He was a practical gentleman, and when the peace terms were agreed upon, it was Francis Lightfoot Lee who insisted that the United States should have the right to navigate the Mississippi and to fish on Newfoundland shores.

Francis Lightfoot Lee   Richard Henry Lee

---

confiscated—*seized and kept by authority*

The first of the signers to die was a Philadelphia judge, John Morton, whose death occurred in April, 1777. Many of his oldest and dearest friends had turned against him because he had signed the Declaration of Independence instead of making peace with the king; and so bitter were they, they refused to be reconciled to Judge Morton even on his death bed. The judge was ill only a few days, and almost with his last breath he spoke these words as his dying message to these old-time friends, "Tell them that they will live to see the hour when they shall acknowledge it to have been the most glorious service that I have ever rendered to my country."

John Morton

John Morton

It is rather surprising that only two of the fifty-six signers met violent deaths, when every one of them considered such an exit from earth highly probable. Button Gwinnett was killed in a duel and Thomas Lynch, Jr., was drowned at sea.

When the latter, a highly educated man from South Carolina, accepted a commission as captain in the American Army, his father insisted that he should not have accepted so low a commission. The son answered, "My present command is fully equal to my experience."

It was the father who was first sent as a delegate to the Continental Congress. He was taken dangerously ill. Thomas begged his superior officer for permission to visit his father but was refused. Fortunately the young man was then sent to Congress from his own state to take the father's place. The father died in his son's arms at Annapolis while trying to reach his home in South Carolina.

Not long after Thomas Lynch signed the Declaration of Independence and was gaining a reputation as

Thomas Lynch Jun

Thomas Lynch Jun!

a statesman, he was taken ill, and in 1779 was sent by his physicians on a sea voyage in the hope of benefiting his health. It is believed that his ship went down in a tempest and was lost with all on board.

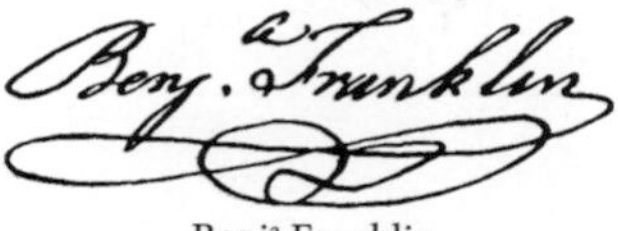

Benj^{a} Franklin

It is rather interesting to learn something of the ages of the men when they signed the Declaration of Independence. Benjamin Franklin, who leads the list of the five oldest, was seventy. Stephen Hopkins was sixty-nine, John Hart was sixty-eight, Francis Lewis was sixty-three, Matthew Thornton was sixty-two, and Philip Livingston was sixty.

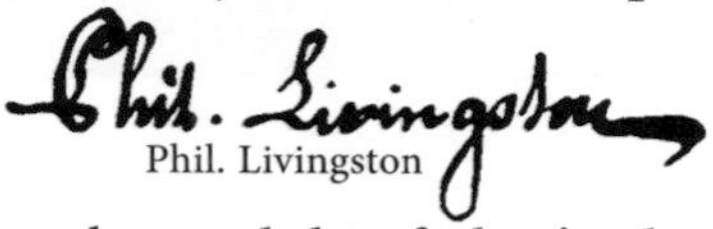

Phil. Livingston

Thomas Lynch, who took his father's place, and Edward Rutledge were only twenty-seven, Thomas Heyward was thirty, Benjamin Rush was thirty-one, Elbridge Gerry was thirty-two, while Thomas Jefferson, Thomas Stone, and Arthur Middleton were thirty-three.

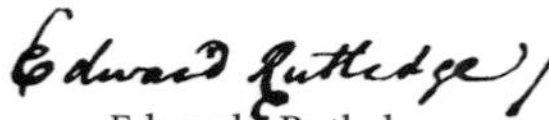

Edward Rutledge

Thos Heyward Junr

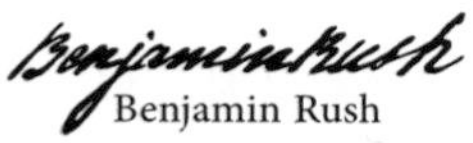

Benjamin Rush

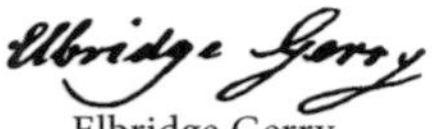

Elbridge Gerry

Thos Stone

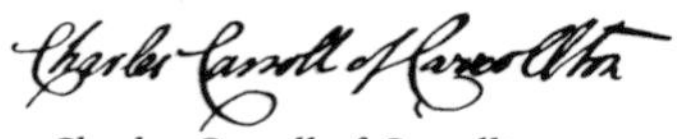

Charles Carroll of Carrollton

Charles Carroll, of Carrollton, is the gentleman who outlived all other signers of the Declaration. On the fourteenth of November, 1832, he died a short time before his ninety-sixth birthday.

It is recorded as a singular fact that twenty-four of the signers, nearly one-half, lived to the age of seventy or over. Fourteen lived on until eighty and no less than five to be ninety or more.

Th Jefferson

Twenty-four of these gentlemen were lawyers, fourteen were farmers, nine were merchants, four were physicians, and although four were educated for the ministry, only one was a clergyman on July 4, 1776, and only one was a manufacturer.

John Sanderson, author of *Biographies of the Signers,* and those who in several volumes completed the work he began, are the best authorities on the subject of the signers of the Declaration of Independence. After a somewhat extensive reading of those biographies, one outstanding fact is noticeable—these men went to their graves with their minds crystal clear.

In an article about the signers of the Declaration of Independence written by Loosing, which may be found in Harper's Magazine for the year 1858, we find these words:

"It is a fact worthy of record that of the fifty-six members of the Continental Congress of 1776, who signed the Declaration of Independence and thereby took a position of great eminence

eminence—*fame*

144

in the sight of the nations, not one fell from his proud estate, either by the effects of political apostasy or lukewarmness or by moral degradation. In public and private life they remained pure; and in that glorious constellation of which the patriot of Monticello is the chief luminary, there is not a single star whose light is dim or unworthy of the highest homage that may be paid to man by the patriot and Christian."

---

estate—*position*
apostasy—*change of belief*

degradation—*corruption*
homage—*a display of respect*

Character Theme—Courage, Loyalty, & Sacrifice

Time to Think

1. How many men signed our Declaration of Independence?
2. Who wrote our Declaration of Independence?
3. Do we still have the original document?
4. Who is John Bull?
5. Why was it so dangerous for the men to sign this document?
6. Why is the story of Robert Morris particularly moving?
7. Who was the oldest signer?
8. Who is "the patriot of Monticello"?
9. Tell about one of the signers that you are going to try to remember.

Let the Nations Be Glad

Psalm 67:1–5

God be merciful unto us, and bless us;
And cause His face to shine upon us.
That Thy way may be known upon earth,
Thy saving health among all nations.
Let the people praise Thee, O God;
Let all the people praise Thee.

O let the nations be glad and sing for joy:
For Thou shalt judge the people righteously,
And govern the nations upon earth.
Let the people praise Thee, O God;
Let all the people praise Thee.

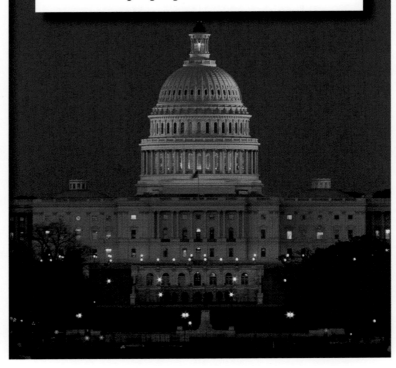

Song of the Settlers

Jessamyn West

Freedom is a hard-bought thing—
A gift no man can give,
For some, a way of dying,
For most, a way to live.

Freedom is a hard-bought thing—
A rifle in the hand,
The horses hitched at sunup,
A harvest in the land.

Freedom is a hard-bought thing—
A massacre, a bloody rout,
The candles lit at nightfall,
And the night shut out.

Freedom is a hard-bought thing—
An arrow in the back,
The wind in the long corn rows,
And the hay in the rack.

Freedom is a way of living,
A song, a mighty cry.
Freedom is the bread we eat;
Let it be the way we die!

---

rout—*an overwhelming defeat*

147

The Landing
of the Pilgrim Fathers

Felicia D. Hemans

The breaking waves dashed high
On a stern and rockbound coast,
And the woods against a stormy sky
Their giant branches tossed,
And the heavy night hung dark
The hills and waters o' er
When a band of exiles moored their bark
On the wild New England shore.

Not as the conqueror comes,
They, the true-hearted, came;
Not with the roll of stirring drums
And the trumpet that sings of fame;
Not as the flying come
In silence and in fear,
They shook the depths of the desert gloom
With their hymns of lofty cheer.

Amidst the storm they sang,
And the stars heard, and the sea;
And the sounding aisles of the dim woods rang
To the anthem of the free.

---

exiles—*those who have been banned
from their country*
bark—*ship*

The ocean eagle soared
From his nest by the white wave's foam,
And the rocking pines of the forest roared;
This was their welcome home.

There were men with hoary hair
Amidst that Pilgrim band;
Why had they come to wither there,
Away from their childhood's land?
There was woman's fearless eye
Lit by her deep love's truth;
There was manhood's brow serenely high
And the fiery heart of youth.

What sought they thus afar?
Bright jewels of the mine,
The wealth of seas, the spoils of war?
They sought a faith's pure shrine.
Aye, call it holy ground,
The soil where first they trod.
They have left unstained what there they found—
Freedom to worship God.

---

hoary—*white or gray*

Sir Hiram of Maine
and the Maxim Dynasty

Harland Manchester

Snowdrifts ten feet high were piled around a remote farmhouse in Upper Abbot, Maine, one night in the late 1850s. Huddled in an old patchwork quilt beside a small kitchen fire sat Mrs. Isaac Maxim, grimly considering the family's situation. The six children had gone to bed hungry. They had been hungry for three weeks. Isaac, who had lost his grist mill and made a precarious living making wooden measures, was away peddling them. When a major snowfall struck northern New England in those days, all commerce and traffic came to a halt. People stayed inside and nursed their fires, waiting to hear the bells from the ox-drawn sledges and the shouts of the rescuing snow-shovelers. Leaving his family with no money and only a little corn meal in the barrel, Isaac had planned to return in a few days with provisions. Now the strictly rationed meal was gone, and the children were chewing spruce gum to keep their jaws busy. Relatives lived not far away, but they had their own problems and the Maxims had their pride.

Early in the morning, Mrs. Maxim awoke to a muffled call. Isaac was outside, tunneling through to the door. In his sleigh were mountains of provisions. Mrs. Maxim cooked a big meal and woke up the children. They ate until they were stuffed, and Isaac, ill and exhausted, fell into bed and slept for a week.

---

precarious—*not secure; risky*   grist mill—*a mill for grinding grain*

Isaac, tall, dark, given to spells of melancholy, was born with an ax in his hands. He could run a lathe, build a wagon, invent gadgets or hoist a two-hundred-pound pork barrel, and once he beat up two highwaymen. He had never gone to school, but he learned to read and spent evenings with the Bible, ancient history, Voltaire, Tom Paine, and books about Napoleon, which he took in barter on his peddling trips. But he couldn't make money. In ten years the Maxims moved eleven times. His wife Harriet, short, muscular and steely-eyed, hoed corn, milked cows, chased the bears away from the sheep, spun, wove, and dyed, cured the sick with barks and herbs, bested a mad dog with her bare hands, and had eight babies. When the children started to toddle, she taught them arithmetic with rows of beans on the kitchen floor.

From this stimulating background emerged a succession of world-renowned inventors, and the greatest of these was the eldest son, Hiram. He invented the Maxim gun, almost beat Edison with the electric light, built one of the first airplanes to leave the ground, and became a rich man and a British knight. His brother Hudson was a leading inventor of smokeless powder and other explosives. Brother Sam made innovations in sewing machines and other devices. Percy, Hiram's son, pioneered in early gas-buggies, and invented the Maxim silencer, and Percy's son Hamilton followed with industrial noise killers. A total of more than 370 patents have been issued to the five inventing Maxims.

The exuberant Maxim children trapped, hunted, fought, wrestled, built dams, water wheels, and boats, and because of Isaac's coaching in craftsmanship, were fascinated by every tool and machine they saw. Deprived of early schooling for lack of decent clothes, they were insatiably curious about the world out-

---

lathe—*a machine that shapes wood by rotating it against a cutting tool*
barter—*the act of trading goods without money*

innovations—*newly introduced ideas*
exuberant—*full of joy*
insatiably—*without satisfaction*

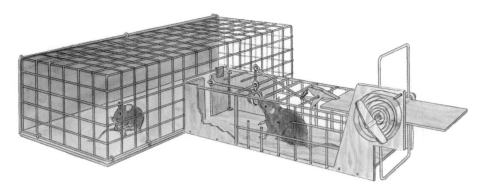

side. Hudson worked in the fields for money to buy a geography book. Hiram wanted to be a sea captain. He couldn't afford a sextant, so he made one from wood and string and spent evenings shooting the North Star. Then he decided to be an artist, made colors from plants and earth, and clipped hair from the baby to make fine brushes.

Hiram turned out his first invention in his father's grist mill. Mice were a problem, and the cage traps then used had to be reset after each capture. With wire from a hoopskirt, Hiram built an automatic trap which could be wound like a clock and would set itself several times, increasing the nightly catch. Then he conceived an idea of making each captive set the trap for the next mouse. The noise of the springing trap scared the mouse, which ran into a storage cage, and in so doing moved a mechanism which reset the trap.

At twenty he left Maine and became a rambling mechanic in northern New York and Canada. He had the frame of an ox, his bellow could be heard a mile, and he reveled in pranks like putting frogs in schoolmasters' water pitchers and mixing phosphorus in people's hair oil so that they glowed at night.

Hiram's serious career started when he went to work in his Uncle Levi's engineering shop at Fitchburg, Massachusetts. Levi manufactured Drake's Gas Machine, which vaporized gasoline

---

sextant—*an instrument used for navigation*
reveled—*took part in celebration*

phosphorus—*a waxy substance that glows in the dark*
vaporized—*having been converted from liquid to gas*

and pumped it through pipes to be burned in jets for illumination. Hiram improved the machine and was soon working in Boston for Oliver Drake, its inventor. He invented—too early to profit by it—an automatic sprinkler that would be started by the heat of a fire. Not appreciated, he went to New York, worked as a draftsman, and in his spare time devised an improved gas illuminating system. There had been trouble keeping the gas mixture even so that the lights would not go dim. This limited the number of lights that could be served by a single machine. Hiram invented a gas-density regulator and other improvements and formed the Maxim Gas Machine Company, which received big contracts. He installed his illuminating system in several New York buildings in the early 1870s, and the great day came when the fifteen hundred rooms of the Grand Union Hotel at Saratoga blazed with Maxim lights.

Hiram was now married, had two children, lived on a proper street in Brooklyn, and wore a full beard and the silk hat and frock coat of a man of position. But he couldn't be dignified. When leaving the house he always vaulted the garden gate, to the distress of his wife and the delight of his small son Hiram Percy. Life with Hiram was never dull. To prove the theory that extremes of heat and cold produce the same sensations, Hiram ostentatiously heated a poker in the kitchen range, secretly cooled another in the icebox, and tested the cool poker on the cook's neck. Mrs. Maxim had to find a new cook. Despite such heartless pranks, Hiram became furious at injustices, and when an itinerant photographer cheated another cook out of two dollars, he spent several Sundays tracking down the swindler. He found him in New Jersey, retrieved the cook's money, and had him arrested and fined. Once he passed a stockyard where the cattle were bellowing from thirst. He charged in, turned on all the faucets, and started a movement to prevent cruelty to cattle.

---

ostentatiously—*boastfully*
itinerant—*one that travels from place to place*

By this time the early electric arc lights were being used, and Edison and Swan of England were trying to perfect an incandescent electric bulb. Attempts were only partially successful because the carbon filaments burned out quickly. Hiram saw that a good bulb would put an end to his gas lights, so he found a partner, formed the United States Electric Lighting Company, and plunged into day-and-night experiments to create a durable lamp. Recalling a phenomenon he had noticed in his gaslight research, he found that if he put a little vaporized gasoline into an airtight bulb with a glowing filament, the carbon produced by the burning vapor would gather on the weak parts of the slender thread and reinforce it. This ingenious discovery greatly lengthened the bulb's life. Hiram finished his first bulb on February 7, 1880, and proudly showed that it would burn under water, a feat then considered miraculous. He did not know that Thomas A. Edison had been granted a broad patent on the carbon-filament electric lamp eleven days before. Though hundreds of thousands of the early lamps were made by Hiram's method, he got nothing out of it. The controversy ended in a long and famous legal battle which Edison won.

---

incandescent—*shining because of heat*
filaments—*fine wires that are heated to produce light*

phenomenon—*something unusual or marvelous*

Hiram remained undaunted, and all manner of original ideas poured from his fertile mind. He had trouble obtaining a rare imported chemical, phosphoric anhydride, which was used to absorb the water vapor in his bulbs. Edison had bought up the available supply. Hiram was no chemist, but in a short time he contrived a method of making the chemical cheaply in large batches. Then there was trouble with the early lighting systems because the bulbs more distant from the station were dimmer. Hiram invented a method of wiring which corrected this condition by insuring constant voltage throughout a lighting system. The new marvels of electric light excited the world, and that year, 1881, a great Electrical Exposition was held in Paris. Maxim demonstrated his new system at the show. It brought him wide acclaim, and the President of the French Republic pinned on his coat the cross of a Chevalier of the Legion of Honor.

Europe offered the forty-one-year-old Yankee Paul Bunyan new worlds to conquer. All about him he saw the need for new machines. A cynical remark made by a visitor at the Paris exhibit fired a new train of thought. "Hang your chemistry and electricity," he was told. "If you want to make a pile of money, invent something that will enable these Europeans to cut one another's throats with greater facility." Maxim remembered the kick of a muzzle-loading shotgun he had used as a boy, and set to work. Two years later, in 1883, he had designed the first automatic machine gun.

While previous machine guns tended to jump about and were somewhat at the mercy of the individual tempo of the operator, Maxim's gun remained steady, with a great improvement in marksmanship. With its single water-cooled barrel and belt-fed cartridges, it was a model of simplicity and efficiency in its day. When the gunner held his finger on the trigger, bullets streamed out at the rate of 666 per minute.

---

contrived—*cleverly planned*　　　　　　**facility**—*ease of motion*
cynical—*characterized by bitterness and unbelief*

The press and the public showed great enthusiasm over the new gun, but military men still stubbornly resisted it. Curiously enough, the gun's chief virtue, rapid fire, was deemed a vice in some quarters. American Army and Navy experts praised it highly as an interesting mechanism, but stated that its appetite for ammunition raised a serious transport problem. The Chinese took the same attitude.

But Hiram Maxim well knew that major military decisions are made by civilians. He was a master showman, and his boyish, outwardly naive exuberance won British hearts. To British eyes, he was what a Yankee ought to be, and he showed due respect for the upper classes. He founded the Maxim Gun Company, later to become Vickers Sons & Maxim, Ltd., and set up a workshop and target range at Hatton Garden. He won the interest of the adventurous Prince of Wales, later Edward VII, who came to the range and fired the gun. There happened to be a photographer present who recorded the event. Several dukes followed suit, and soon it became the rage among the British smart set to make the pilgrimage to Hatton Garden and fire the Maxim gun. Maxim estimated that more than two hundred thousand cartridges were fired during the London social season, and he considered the money well spent.

---

deemed—*considered to be*

The British government placed an order, and soon Maxim was on the road to fame and wealth. He toured Europe, easily winning competitions with other gunmakers. In one of these contests, on an Austrian target range, Emperor Franz Josef appeared unexpectedly. With great presence of mind, Maxim hung up a fresh paper target and neatly perforated it with the initials "F. J.," not forgetting the dots. The Emperor was pleased and later an order was booked. There is a story that Kaiser Wilhelm II fired the gun in person at a machine-gun competition at Spandau, Germany, that he was exhilarated to discover that he could sweep the gun like garden hose, and that onlookers became very jittery.

Back in Maine when Hiram was a boy, his father Isaac had fiddled with plans for flying machines. In 1893, while on a cruise in the Mediterranean, Hiram became interested in air currents and bird flights and went home with plans to put man in the air. Using surprisingly precocious concepts, he built experimental wings and propellers and tested them on a spinning turntable which served as a kind of wind tunnel. He built the lightest steam engine possible and assembled his plane on a forty-acre field, with steel launching tracks and a tethering device for limiting flight tests. On a trial run it bounded forward, rose from the tracks and broke loose, and for a brief moment Sir Hiram was airborne. Then a propeller hit an object, the machine was wrecked, and he abandoned the costly project. Many people believed that he was on the way toward building a workable plane, but that some of his ideas were unsound. Later the Wright brothers profited by his detailed reports.

During the thirty years of Hiram Maxim's greatest productivity, hardly a year elapsed in which he was not granted several patents either in England or the United States. The diversity of his interests and the speed with which he translated his ideas

precocious—*premature; unusually early in development*

into working devices was amazing. His first patented invention, in 1866, was an improved iron for curling hair. Among his other inventions were carburetors, meters, pumps, chandeliers, motor governors, stone-cutting machines, vacuum cleaners, ship stabilizers, railway wheels, pneumatic tires, fire extinguishers, an improved blackboard, a compressed air gun for torpedoes, riveting machines, and coffee substitutes. He was also a pioneer in the field of explosive mixtures and smokeless powders.

In 1912, after a study of the guidance mechanism of bats, he suggested a subsonic siren for ships by which they could locate surrounding objects by echoes, like the sonar system now used by submarines. He died in 1916 at the age of seventy-six, soon after patenting a process for cracking heavy oils to make gasoline—a technique indispensable in providing fuel for today's automobiles.

Sir Hiram was dead, but Isaac of Maine had founded a dynasty of inventors, and the Maxim genius marched on. Three of the brothers had died early, two of them in the Civil War. Sam stayed on the farm, patented oil lamps, ironing boards and sewing machine improvements, and read to the family in the evenings. Hudson, the sixth child, who had changed his name from Isaac, grew up like Hiram with bulging muscles, a fearless disposition, and a burning passion for knowledge and adventure. At fifteen he was walking miles through snowdrifts to district schools and throwing all comers in wrestling matches at county fairs. Hiram asked him to come to New York and help him with his gas machines. Hudson arrived in a lumberman's shirt and a knitted cap made by his mother. A circus bought one of Hiram's lighting systems, and Hudson traveled with the show to operate it. He loved to ride in the parade, wearing armor and a plumed helmet. He invaded New York's Houston Street wrestling section, called "Murderer's Row," and threw several pros.

---

pneumatic—*relating to air or gases*   subsonic—*slower than the speed of sound*

A promoter tried to sign him up, but he wanted more schooling and returned to Maine. There he enrolled in a boarding school, working in a quarry and selling books to pay expenses. After he finished school, he was offered a teaching vacancy on the condition that he take care of a tough boy who had thrown the latest incumbent out the window. Hudson won the decision in one round, and the job was his.

Hudson operated a publishing firm and explored various other callings, but he was never quite happy until he began experimenting with deadly mixtures which went off with a loud bang. He worked for Hiram in England for a time, found the same hemisphere too small for them, and came home with samples of foreign gunpowders. He discovered a rotting shack near the Hoosac Tunnel in western Massachusetts, where explosives had been stored, and collected driblets of nitroglycerin from old tin cans for his experiments. After he married and moved to Brooklyn, things sometimes went off in his backyard laboratory. To prove that explosives were harmless if handled correctly, he would light things with a stick of dynamite and burn nitroglycerin to heat a chafing dish. The neighbors still were doubtful.

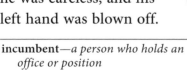

Needing more room for his violent pets, Hudson took over a small plant in a deserted area of New Jersey, which he later renamed Maxim. There explosions were commonplace, as he tested all manner of mixtures. Once he was careless, and his left hand was blown off.

incumbent—*a person who holds an office or position*

Assaulted by a ruffian a few weeks later, he knocked him out with his right.

Hudson invented and patented several new and more powerful explosives and became recognized as a leading authority. The invention that made him famous was the perfection of an efficient smokeless powder for large guns. The stick of smokeless powder then used could not push the projectile from the barrel fast enough, because it lacked the burning surface needed to maintain high pressure as the projectile moved forward and made more room in the barrel. Mixing explosive cakes of various kinds, Hudson put holes in them to make them burn faster. His perforated powder sticks were adopted by the Army and Navy. The du Pont Company bought Hudson's patents and hired him as consultant, and he continued to make profitable loud noises.

During World War I Hudson was chairman of the committee on ordnance and explosives of the Naval Consulting Board, examining thousands of inventions submitted to the Navy. He was himself granted seventy-four patents for explosives and machines to make them, for torpedoes, time fuses, a steam cooker, and a road-building machine. As early as 1875 Hudson had written a speculative paper, "Principles of Force and Demonstration of the Existence of the Atom," in which he postulated the compound nature of the atom. He speculated about solar power, proposed the heated pavements now in use to melt snow, and suggested the distant showing of Broadway plays by something he called "teleview." As a schoolboy he had memorized Pope's "Essay on Man" and all his life recited long passages. Once in a public debate he was preceded by an opponent whose arguments were senseless, but whose delivery was impressive. In Hudson's rebuttal, he convulsed the audience by running the complete gamut of emotions while repeating the vowels, a, e, i, o, u.

---

ordnance—*military equipment*
postulated—*declared as truth*
rebuttal—*a statement that declares an
    opposing argument*

convulsed—*caused laughter in*
gamut—*a complete series or range*

One day in 1894, a crowd gathered in Lynn, Massachusetts, to see a studious young man named Hiram Percy Maxim ride a weird, sputtering vehicle down a hill. The motor-driven tricycle collapsed, threw its inventor, and died in the gutter. A Boston upbringing and an M.I.T. education had combed the Maxim burrs out of old Hiram's son Percy, but in mechanical enterprise he was a chip off the old block. A cyclist, he thought it would be a simple matter to build a small gasoline motor to push the pedals for him. The crude motor he constructed was so heavy that three wheels were needed to support it. Soon he was mounting his engines in buggies. Haynes, Winton, Ford, and many others were similarly engaged, but Percy hadn't heard of them. Nor had he heard of a gearshift, a differential, a spark plug or a cooling system; he counted on taking care of such minor details on a dull afternoon in the electrical shop where he worked.

One of the few men who did not think Percy crazy was Colonel Albert A. Pope, Hartford bicycle manufacturer. He hired him to develop a practical motor vehicle. Fashioning and refashioning by trial and error the many ingenious automobile parts which we now take for granted, Percy assembled his gas-buggies and tested them over rutty roads, carrying tools and spare parts and a chart showing the location of blacksmith shops. By a miracle of imaginative craftsmanship, he turned out within four years a car that ran from Hartford to Boston and back and beat a Stanley Steamer in a race. Soon Pope was leading the country in the building of motor carriages, both gasoline and electric. The first city taxicab fleets were composed of Maxim-designed electric vehicles.

When the pioneer work was done, big business moved in, and Percy Maxim was not dealt into the game. He was casting about for new worlds to conquer when a friend made a sug-

---

M.I.T.—*Massachusetts Institute of Technology*

gestion. Hiram had invented rapid-fire guns and Hudson had eliminated the smoke which betrayed their position. Why not complete the job by silencing the guns, so that the enemy would have no clue to the origin of projectiles? This seemed fantastic, but Percy thought it over. Like Archimedes, he found the answer in his bathtub. The whirling motion of water going down the drain suggested a spiral gadget to whirl the gases leaving a gun barrel, slowing them down and killing the noise. This was the origin of the world-famous Maxim silencer. The gun silencer was never a commercial success; military men considered it impractical and civil authorities banned it as an aid to criminals. But it made its inventor a pioneer in the important new business of killing nerve-shattering industrial noises.

About this time Percy's son, Hiram Hamilton finished at M.I.T. and joined forces with his father. In the 1920s the highly efficient oil-burning diesel engine was being adapted for cargo vessels, but the noise of the exhaust was unbearable. The Maxims invented big cylinders containing sound traps which were attached to the exhaust pipes. They were widely adopted. Percy died in 1936, and Hamilton carried on the work. More than half the vessels in America's World War II navy were diesel-powered, and nine out of ten of them were quieted by Maxim silencers. Without these devices, troops on landing craft could not have heard orders above the din, and surfacing submarines would have announced their presence to craft miles away. In the early days of jet engines, their terrific roar on the testing stands made factory workers sick. Now Maxim silencers have cut the shout to a whisper.

Private diesel-electric plants in many large hospitals, department stores, and office buildings run quietly because of the work of Percy and Hamilton. During the war, automatic cannons equipped with Maxim silencers were tried out in the basement of the Colt factory in Hartford without disturbing the general manager, whose office was directly overhead. Hamilton also worked on improved snow-moving equipment, and to clear his driveway in Farmington, Connecticut, built a light V-shaped plow which he attached to the bumper of his car. A genuine Maxim, he made and sold several thousand of them.

All these ideas must have appealed to old Isaac, gazing down from his celestial workbench at the breed of men he sired.

Character Theme—Initiative &
Resourcefulness

Time to Think

1. Of the six children of Isaac and Harriet Maxim, which one was the greatest inventor?
2. Even though the Maxim children did not go to school, what character trait did they have that helped them get an education?
3. What was Hiram's first invention?
4. Who profited from Hiram's reports on his flying machine?
5. What was Hiram's first invention to be patented?
6. Which of Hiram's brothers loved working with explosives?

The Great Stone Face

Nathaniel Hawthorne
(adapted by Tracy Glockle)

One afternoon, when the sun was going down, a mother and her little boy sat at the door of their cottage, talking about the Great Stone Face. They had only to lift their eyes, and there it could be plainly seen, though miles away, with the sunshine brightening all its features. The Great Stone Face was formed on the steep side of a mountain by some huge rocks that resembled a human face. All the features were noble, grand, and sweet.

"Mother," said the child, whose name was Ernest, "If I were to see a man with such a face, I should love him dearly."

"If an old prophecy comes to pass," answered his mother, "we may see a man with exactly such a face as that."

"What prophecy do you mean, dear Mother?" eagerly inquired Ernest.

So his mother told him a story that her own mother had told to her when she herself was younger than little Ernest. A story so old that even the Indians, who had once lived in the valley, had heard the story from their forefathers. Some day, a child should be born nearby who was destined to become the greatest and noblest person of his time, and whose countenance in manhood would look exactly like the Great Stone Face.

"O Mother, dear Mother!" cried Ernest, clapping his hands, "I do hope that I shall live to see him!"

"Perhaps you may," his mother said to him.

Ernest never forgot the story that his mother told him. He spent his childhood in the log-cottage where he was born, assisting his mother much with his little hands and even more with his loving heart. He grew up to be a quiet, unnoticed boy, sunbrowned with labor in the fields, but with more intelligence than many lads who have been taught at famous schools. Yet Ernest had had no teacher, except that the Great Stone Face became one to him. When his work was done, he would gaze at it for hours, until he began to imagine that those vast features recognized him and gave him a smile.

About this time there went a rumor throughout the valley that the great man, foretold for ages, who was to resemble the Great Stone Face, had appeared at last. Many years before, a young man had left the valley and settled at a distant seaport where, after getting together a little money, he had become a shopkeeper. His name—whether it was his real one, or a nickname—was Gathergold. He became an exceedingly rich merchant, and owner of a whole fleet of ships. It might be said of him, as of Midas in the fable, that whatever he touched was changed at once into piles of gold coins. And when Mr. Gather-

---

countenance—*face or expression on it*

gold had become very rich, he remembered his native valley and resolved to go back there. He sent a skilled architect to build him a palace fit for a man of his vast wealth.

People were even more ready to believe that Mr. Gathergold was the prophetic person so long and vainly looked for when they saw the splendid building that rose as if by magic on the site of his father's old weatherbeaten farmhouse.

Our friend Ernest, meanwhile, was deeply stirred by the idea that the great, noble man of prophecy was to be made known. He knew, boy though he was, that there were a thousand ways in which Mr. Gathergold, with his vast wealth, might become an angel of kindness. While the boy was still gazing up the valley and fancying that the Great Stone Face looked kindly back at him, the rumbling of wheels was heard approaching swiftly along the winding road.

"Here he comes!" cried a group of people. "Here comes the great Mr. Gathergold!"

A carriage drawn by four horses dashed around the turn of the road. Within it, thrust partly out of the window, appeared the face of the old man, his skin as yellow as if his own Midas-hand had changed it. He had a low forehead, small sharp eyes, and very thin lips which he made still thinner by pressing them together.

As the carriage rolled onward, an old woman and two little children held out their hands and begged most piteously. A yellow hand poked itself out of the coach-window, and dropped some copper coins upon the ground; so that the great man's name might just as suitably have been Scattercopper. Nevertheless, with as much good faith as ever, the people shouted—

"He is the very image of the Great Stone Face!"

And what greatly puzzled Ernest, they seemed actually to believe that here was the likeness. But Ernest turned sadly from the hardness of that greedy face, and gazed up at the

valley where he could still see those glorious features. The face cheered him. What did the kind lips seem to say?

"He will come! Fear not, Ernest; the man will come!"

Years sped swiftly and quietly away. Ernest, now a man of middle age, still dwelt in his native valley. Gradually, he had become known among the people. He was the same simple-hearted man, but he had given so many of the best hours of his life for some great good to mankind, that it seemed as though he had received a portion of the angels' wisdom. Almost involuntarily, too, he had become a preacher. His pure, simple thoughts took shape in the good deeds that dropped silently from his hand and flowed forth in speech. He uttered truths that molded the lives of those who heard him. His hearers never suspected that Ernest was more than an ordinary man; least of all did Ernest himself suspect it.

By this time poor Mr. Gathergold was dead and buried. His wealth had disappeared before his death. Since then, it had been very generally admitted that there was no resemblance, after all, between the snobbish features of the ruined merchant and that majestic face upon the mountainside. So the people ceased to honor him.

But now again there were reports in the newspapers, affirming that the likeness of the Great Stone Face had appeared upon the broad shoulders of a certain famous statesman. He, like Mr. Gathergold, was a native of the valley, but had left it in his early days, and taken up the trades of law and politics. So wonderfully eloquent was he, that whatever he might choose to say, his listeners had no choice but to believe him; wrong looked like right, and right like wrong. Truly, he was a wondrous man; and when his tongue had acquired for him all other imaginable success, it finally persuaded his countrymen to select him for the Presidency. As soon as he began to grow famous, his admirers had found the resemblance between him and the Great Stone Face so great that throughout the country he was known as Old Stony Phiz.

While his friends were doing their best to make him President, Old Stony Phiz set out on a visit to the valley where he was born. Magnificent preparations were made to receive the statesman; horsemen set forth to meet him at the boundary line of the state, and all the people left their work and gathered along the wayside to see him pass. Among these was Ernest. Though disappointed before, he had such a hopeful and trusting nature. So now again, he went to see the likeness of the Great Stone Face.

It really was a very brilliant spectacle. The people were throwing up their hats and shouting with enthusiasm so contagious that Ernest likewise threw up his hat and shouted as loudly as the loudest, "Hurray for the great man! Hurray for Old Stony Phiz!" But as yet he had not seen him.

"Here he is, now!" cried those who stood near Ernest.

In an open carriage drawn by four white horses, with his large head uncovered, sat the illustrious statesman, Old Stony Phiz himself.

---

affirm—*to agree that something is true*   illustrious—*famous*
eloquent—*ability to speak in a persuasive way*

"Confess it," said one of Ernest's neighbors to him, "The Great Stone Face has met his match at last!"

At his first glimpse, Ernest did fancy that there was a resemblance. But the divine sympathy that enlightened the face on the mountain could not be found here. Something had been originally left out, or had departed. And therefore the marvelously gifted statesman always had a weary gloom in his eyes, like a man whose life, with all its high accomplishments, was meaningless and empty because no high purpose had enriched it.

Still, Ernest's neighbor thrust his elbow into his side, and pressed him for an answer.

"Confess! Confess! Is not he the very picture of your Old Man of the Mountain?"

"No!" said Ernest, bluntly, "I see little or no likeness."

"Then so much the worse for the Great Stone Face!" answered his neighbor, and again he set up a shout for Old Stony Phiz.

But Ernest turned away, sad and almost discouraged; for this was the saddest of his disappointments, to behold a man who might have fulfilled the prophecy and had chosen not to do so. Meantime, the procession swept past him, leaving the dust to settle and the Great Stone Face to be revealed.

The kind lips seemed to say, "I have waited longer than you, and am not yet weary. Fear not; the man will come."

The years hurried onward, and now they began to bring white hairs and scatter them over Ernest's head. But he had not grown old in vain: more than the white hairs on his head were the wise thoughts in his mind. And Ernest had stopped being unknown. College professors and even the active men of cities, came from afar to see and speak with Ernest; for the report had gone abroad that this simple farmer had ideas unlike those of other men—not gained from books, but of a higher tone—as if he had been talking with angels. Ernest received these visitors with the gentle sincerity that had characterized him from boyhood, and spoke freely with them. Thoughtful after speaking with him, his guests went their way and, as they passed up the valley, paused to look at the Great Stone Face, imagining that they had seen its likeness in a human face, but could not remember where.

While Ernest had been growing old, Providence had granted a new poet to this earth. He, likewise, was a native of the valley, but had spent the greater part of his life at a distance from that romantic region. Often, however, the mountains, which had been familiar to him in his childhood, lifted their snowy peaks into his poetry. Neither was the Great Stone Face forgotten, for the poet had written about it in a poem which was grand enough to have been uttered by its own majestic lips.

The songs of this poet found their way to Ernest. He read them after his toil, seated on the bench before his cottage door, where for so long he had filled his rest by gazing at the Great Stone Face. As he read stanzas that caused his soul to thrill within him, he lifted his eyes to the vast countenance beaming on him so kindly.

Now it happened that the poet, though he dwelt so far away, had heard of Ernest, and desired to meet this man whose untaught wisdom walked hand in hand with his life. One summer morning, therefore, he traveled by train, arriving in the late afternoon not far from Ernest's cottage.

Approaching the door, he found the good old man holding a volume in his hand, which he read, and then, looked lovingly at the Great Stone Face.

"Good evening," said the poet. "Can you give a traveler a night's lodging?"

"Willingly," answered Ernest, smiling.

The poet sat down on the bench beside him, and he and Ernest talked together. Never before had the poet talked with a man like Ernest, who combined the exalted ideas of angels with

---

Providence—*referring to God*

the sweet and lowly charm of simple words. Ernest, on the other hand, was moved and excited by the images which the poet flung out of his mind, images which seemed to fill all the air with shapes of beauty.

"Who are you, my strangely gifted guest?" Ernest asked.

The poet laid his finger on the volume that Ernest had been reading. "I wrote these poems," he said.

Ernest examined the poet's face; then turned toward the Great Stone Face; then back again to his guest. But his countenance fell; he shook his head, and sighed.

"Why are you sad?" inquired the poet.

"Because," replied Ernest, "all through life I have awaited the fulfillment of a prophecy; and, when I read these poems, I hoped that it might be fulfilled in you."

"Yes, Ernest, it is my doom," answered the poet. "You must record another failure of your hopes. I am not worthy to resemble that kind and majestic image."

"And why?" asked Ernest.

"My life, dear Ernest, has not corresponded with my thought." The poet spoke sadly, and his eyes were dim with tears. So were Ernest's eyes.

At the hour of sunset, as had long been his custom, Ernest was to talk to a gathering of the neighboring inhabitants in the open air. He and the poet, still talking together as they went along, proceeded to the spot. Ernest looked with familiar kindness at his audience gathered upon the grass.

He began to speak, giving to the people what was in his heart and mind. His words had power because they agreed with his life. The poet, as he listened, gazed reverently at the noble man, and thought that there never was a face as mild, sweet, and thoughtful, with the glory of white hair about it. At a distance, but easily seen in the golden light of the setting sun, appeared the Great Stone Face, with white mists around it like the white hairs of Ernest. At that moment, the poet threw up his arms and shouted—

"Behold! Behold! Ernest is the likeness of the Great Stone Face!"

Then all the people saw that what the poet said was true. The prophecy was fulfilled. But Ernest, having finished what he had to say, took the poet's arm, and walked slowly homeward, still hoping that some wiser and better man than himself would by and by appear, bearing a resemblance to the Great Stone Face.

Until 2003 when the rock formation collapsed, the Old Man of the Mountain could be seen in the White Mountains of New Hampshire.

Character Theme—Wisdom

Time to Think

1. Who or what became a teacher for Ernest?
2. What was the prophecy of the Great Stone Face?
3. What did Mr. Gathergold represent? Old Stony Phiz? The poet?
4. Who did the people finally realize was the fulfillment of the prophecy of the Great Stone Face?

LIBERTY

James Russell Lowell

Our fathers fought for Liberty,
They struggled long and well,
History of their deeds can tell—
But did they leave us free?

Are we free from vanity,
Free from pride, and free from self,
Free from love of power and pelf,
From everything that's beggarly?

Are we free from stubborn will,
From low hate and malice small,
From opinion's tyrant thrall?
Are none of us our own slaves still?

Are we free to speak our thought,
To be happy, and be poor,
Free to enter Heaven's door,
To live and labor as we ought?

Are we then made free at last
From the fear of what men say,
Free to reverence Today,
Free from slavery of the Past?

Our fathers fought for Liberty,
They struggled long and well,
History of their deeds can tell—
But ourselves must set us free.

---

pelf—*money*   **thrall**—*a slave*

MEET THE AUTHOR

Mr. Lowell spent much of his early adulthood
writing poetry. Because of his opposition to
slavery, he also wrote and edited articles to
persuade Americans that slavery was wrong.

173

The Building of the Ship

Henry Wadsworth Longfellow

"The Building of the Ship" is the title of a long poem written by Henry Wadsworth Longfellow in 1849. It tells of a merchant who hired a shipbuilder to build him a ship to carry his merchandise.

"Build me straight, O worthy Master!
Stanch and strong, a goodly vessel,
That shall laugh at all disaster
And with wave and whirlwind wrestle!"

The poem tells how the Master built that ship.

"Thus," said he, "will we build this ship!
Lay square the blocks upon the slip,
And follow well this plan of mine.
Choose the timbers with greatest care;
Of all that is unsound beware;
For only what is sound and strong
To this vessel shall belong.
Cedar of Maine and Georgia pine
Here together all combine;
A goodly frame, and a goodly fame,
And the UNION be her name!"

As this ship took form and grew "stanch and strong,"
the poet saw it more and more as a symbol of this country.

Behold, at last,
Each tall and tapering mast
Is swung into its place . . .
And at the masthead,
White, blue, and red,
A flag unrolls the stripes and stars,
Ah! when the wanderer, lonely, friendless,
In foreign harbors shall behold
That flag unrolled,
'Twill be as a friendly hand . . .

---

stanch—*staunch, of strong construction*
masthead—*the top of a mast that holds a ship's sails*

As the ship was finished, it no longer symbolized the nation but personified it. Longfellow's concluding lines became famous.

> Thou, too, sail on, O Ship of State!
> Sail on, O UNION, strong and great!
> Humanity with all its fears,
> With all the hopes of future years,
> Is hanging breathless on thy fate!

---

personified—*was a perfect example of*

We know what Master laid thy keel,
What Workmen wrought thy ribs of steel,
Who made each mast, and sail, and rope,
What anvils rang, what hammers beat,
In what a forge and what a heat
Were shaped the anchors of thy hope!
Fear not each sudden sound and shock,
'Tis of the wave and not the rock;
'Tis but the flapping of the sail,
And not a rent made by the gale!
In spite of rock and tempest's roar,
In spite of false lights on the shore,
Sail on, nor fear to breast the sea!
Our hearts, our hopes, are all with thee,
Our hearts, our hopes, our prayers, our tears,
Our faith triumphant o'er our fears,
Are all with thee—are all with thee!

During England's darkest days of World War II, when the remnants of her armies had been rescued from Dunkirk, when bombs fell on London every night, the United States extended a "friendly hand" in the form of weapons and supplies. President Roosevelt met British Prime Minister Churchill and promised to help his people in every way possible. We became the "arsenal of democracy."

With our technical skills and our vast natural resources and our firm faith in the triumph of the right, we were able to send what was needed to keep the enemy from invading England.

And with the guns and tanks and prayers President Roosevelt sent these words:

Humanity with all its fears,
With all the hopes of future years,
Is hanging breathless on thy fate!

---

keel—*the structural support of a boat*
forge—*furnace*
arsenal—*a building that stores supplies*

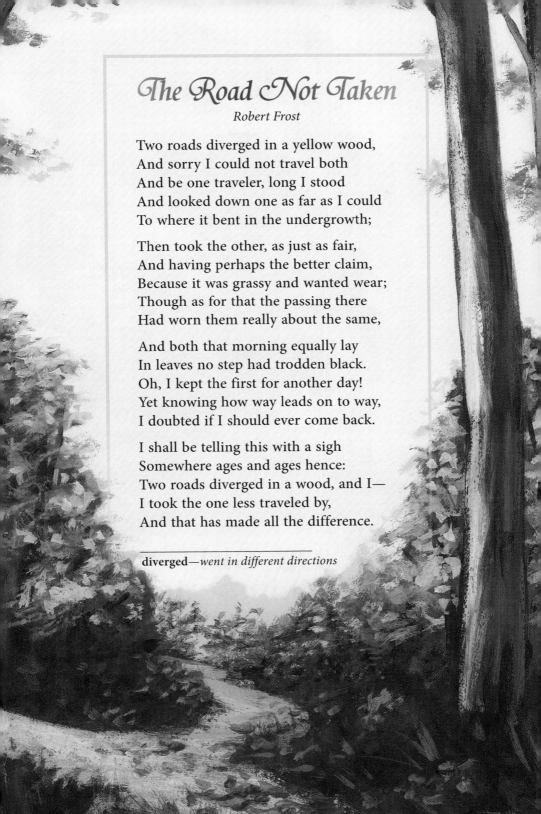

The Road Not Taken

Robert Frost

Two roads diverged in a yellow wood,
And sorry I could not travel both
And be one traveler, long I stood
And looked down one as far as I could
To where it bent in the undergrowth;

Then took the other, as just as fair,
And having perhaps the better claim,
Because it was grassy and wanted wear;
Though as for that the passing there
Had worn them really about the same,

And both that morning equally lay
In leaves no step had trodden black.
Oh, I kept the first for another day!
Yet knowing how way leads on to way,
I doubted if I should ever come back.

I shall be telling this with a sigh
Somewhere ages and ages hence:
Two roads diverged in a wood, and I—
I took the one less traveled by,
And that has made all the difference.

---

diverged—*went in different directions*

The Girl
of the Limberlost

Gene Stratton-Porter (adapted)

Elnora Comstock liked nothing better than collecting the moths, butterflies, and cocoons which she found around the outskirts of the Limberlost swamp near her home. Her life was hard, and this was all the pleasure she had except that of going to a country school. But now she had finished the highest grade in the school.

Elnora had ambition, and she intended to go to high school at any cost, but her mother discouraged her, telling her they could not afford it. However, Elnora insisted upon going, and on the day the city high school opened for the autumn term she walked to town, wearing an ugly brown calico dress and heavy shoes.

This first day was full of troubles for Elnora. The girls laughed at her clothes. She found that she had to buy the books which she thought would be furnished by the school. She also learned that she must pay tuition fees. Oh, it was a gloomy day! But there was one ray of light. The teacher of the algebra class told her that her explanation of a problem was perfect. So Elnora went home resolved to overcome all the obstacles in her way; how she could do this she did not know.

At four o'clock the next morning Elnora was shelling beans. By six she had fed the chickens and pigs, swept two of the rooms of the cabin, built a fire, and put on the kettle. Then she climbed the narrow stairs to the attic she had occupied since she was a small child, dressed in the hated shoes and brown calico, plastered down her crisp curls, ate what breakfast she could, and, putting on her hat, started for town.

"There is no reason in your going for an hour yet," said her mother.

"I must try to find some way to earn those books," replied Elnora. "I am certain I shall not pick them up in the road wrapped in tissue paper."

She went toward the city, as on the day before. Her worry as to where tuition and books were

calico—*a rough cotton cloth*

to come from was greater than it had been then, but she did not feel quite so miserable in other ways. Never again would she have to face all the humiliation for the first time. She had been through it once and it could never be so bad as it was on that first day.

She stopped at her "tree box" in the swamp, rearranged her hair, and left the tin pail in the box as she had done the preceding day. This time she folded two sandwiches in a napkin and tied them in a neat paper parcel which she carried in her hand. Then she hurried along the road to town and found a bookstore. There she asked the prices of the books on her list and learned that six dollars would not quite supply them. She anxiously inquired for second-hand books, but was told that the only way to secure them was from the last year's freshmen. At that moment Elnora felt that nothing could induce her to approach any of the students who she supposed were sophomores and ask to buy their old books. The only balm the girl could see for the humiliation of the day before was to appear at school with a set of new books.

"Do you wish these?" asked the clerk hurriedly, for the store was rapidly filling with school children.

"Yes," gasped Elnora, "oh, yes! but I cannot pay for them just now. Please let me take them, and I will pay for them on Friday or return them in perfect condition. Please trust me for a few days."

The clerk looked at her doubtfully and asked for her name. "I will speak to the proprietor," he said. When he came back Elnora knew the answer before he spoke. "I am sorry," he said, "but Mr. Hann does not recognize your name. You are not a customer of ours and he feels that he cannot take the risk. You will have to bring the money."

Elnora clumped out of the store, the thump of her heavy shoes beating on her brain like a hammer. She tried two other

---

proprietor—*owner of a business*

stores with the same result and then sick at heart came into the street. What could she do? She was too frightened to think. Should she lose that day from school and try to sell beds of wild ferns to the wealthy people of the town, as she had thought of doing? What would she dare ask for bringing in and planting a clump of ferns? How could she carry them? Would people buy them? As she considered these problems she slowly moved down the street. Suddenly she roused herself and glanced around to see if there was a clock anywhere, for she felt sure that the boys and girls passing her in groups were on their way to school.

And there in the bank window, in big black letters, was a sign that made her heart leap:

WANTED
Caterpillars, Cocoons, Chrysalides,
Pupae Cases, Butterflies, Moths,
Indian Relics of all kinds.
Highest scale of prices paid in cash.

Elnora went into the bank and caught the gate at the cashier's desk with both hands to brace herself against disappointment. "Who is it that wants to buy cocoons, butterflies, and moths?" she panted.

"The Bird Woman," answered the cashier. "Have you some for sale?"

"I have some but I do not know whether they are what she wants," Elnora replied.

"Well, you had better see her," said the cashier. "Do you know where she lives?"

"Yes," answered Elnora. "Can you tell me what time it is?"

"Twenty-one after eight," was the answer.

She had nine minutes in which to reach the auditorium. If she did not go at once she would be late. Should she go to school or to the Bird Woman? Several girls passed her, walking swiftly, and she remembered their faces. They were hurrying to school. Elnora decided to hurry too; she would see the Bird Woman at noon. Algebra was the first lesson she would have and the teacher of that subject was kind. Perhaps she could find the superintendent and ask him for a book for the next lesson, and at noon—"O dear Lord, make it come true," prayed Elnora— perhaps at noon she could sell some of those wonderful shining-winged things she had been collecting all her life on the outskirts of the Limberlost.

As she went down the long hall she saw the algebra teacher standing in the door of his recitation room. When she came up to him he smiled and spoke to her. "I have been watching for you," he said.

Elnora stopped, bewildered. "For me?" she asked.

"Yes," replied Mr. Henley. "Come inside."

Elnora followed him into the room and he closed the door behind them. Then he said, "At our teachers' meeting yesterday afternoon one of the teachers told of a pupil who had shown in class that she had expected her books to be furnished by the city. I thought that possibly it was you. Was it?"

"Yes," breathed Elnora.

"I thought so," said Mr. Henley, "and it occurred to me that since you had not expected to buy the books you might require a little time to secure them. You have too much ability in algebra to be permitted to fall behind for want of supplies; so I telephoned one of our sophomores to bring her last year's books this morning. I am sorry to say that they are somewhat abused, but none of the pages are missing. You may have the books for two dollars and pay when you can. Here they are. Would you care to take them?"

Elnora sat down suddenly because she could not stand another instant. She reached both hands for the books without saying a word. Mr. Henley was silent also. At last Elnora arose, hugging the books to her heart as a mother clasps a baby that has been lost and just restored to her arms.

"One thing more," said Mr. Henley. "You can pay your tuition fees quarterly. You need not bother about the first installment this month. Any time in October will do."

It seemed as if Elnora's gasp of relief must have reached the soles of her heavy shoes. "Did anyone ever tell you how beautiful you are?" she cried.

As the teacher was lank, ugly, and so nearsighted that he peered at his pupils through spectacles, no one ever had. "No," said Mr. Henley, "I have waited a long time for the information; for that reason I appreciate it all the more. Come, or we shall be late for opening exercises."

So Elnora entered the auditorium a second time. Her face was like the brightest dawn that ever broke over the Limberlost. No matter about the lumbering shoes and calico dress now; no matter about anything. She had the books; she could take them home. In her garret she could commit them to memory if need be. She would show that clothes are not everything. If the Bird Woman did not want any of the many different kinds of specimens she had collected, she was quite sure now she could sell ferns, nuts, and a great many things. As she took a seat a girl

---

lank—*tall and thin, appearing awkward*
garret—*a room on the top floor of a house,
   usually under a pitched roof*

moved over to make room for her, something no one had done the day before, and several girls smiled and bowed. This change had been brought about by one more thoughtful than the rest who had talked to the others about their treatment of Elnora, and now all was different. But the happy Elnora forgot everything except her books and that she was in school and could learn the many things she longed to know.

At noon Elnora took her parcel of lunch and went to the Bird Woman's home. She must know about the specimens first, and then she would go out to the suburbs somewhere and eat the sandwiches. As she dropped the heavy iron knocker on the door of the big red log cabin her heart thumped at the resounding stroke.

"Is the Bird Woman at home?" she asked the maid.

"She is at lunch," was the answer.

"Please ask her if she will see a girl from the Limberlost about some moths," Elnora said.

"If it is about moths I need not ask," laughed the girl. "Our orders are to admit anyone with specimens at any time. Come this way."

Elnora went down a wide hall and entered a beautiful room with an old English fireplace. In the corners there were closets filled with rare pieces of china. At a bare table of shining oak sat a woman Elnora had often watched and followed secretly around the Limberlost. It was the Bird Woman and she was holding out a hand of welcome.

"I heard the maid!" she laughingly said. "A little pasteboard box or just the word 'specimen' passes anyone through my door. I hope you have hundreds of moths. I have been so busy all summer that I have been unable to do any collecting, and I need many specimens. Sit down and have lunch with me while we talk it over. Did you say that you are from the Limberlost?"

"I live near the swamp," replied Elnora.

"What have you collected?" asked the Bird Woman, as she offered Elnora sandwiches unlike any she had ever before tasted, salad that seemed to be made of many familiar things but you were sure only of celery and apples, and a cup of hot chocolate which would have delighted any hungry schoolgirl.

Elnora said, "Thank you," and tried to eat the things before her, but her eyes were on the Bird Woman's face. "I am afraid I am bothering you for nothing and wasting your time," she said. "That 'collected' frightens me. I have only 'gathered.' I have always loved everything outdoors and so I made friends and playmates of all live things. When I learned that moths die so soon I collected and mounted them because there seemed to be no harm in doing so."

"I feel the same way about it," said the Bird Woman encouragingly. She saw that the girl could not eat until she knew whether her moths would be bought so she asked Elnora if she knew what kinds she had.

"I do not know all of them," answered Elnora. "Before Mr. Duncan moved away he often saw me near the edge of the swamp, and he showed me a box he had made and gave me the key. In it he put books and other things that would help me. From that time on I studied and tried to find the most beautiful moths. I also tried to capture and mount them in the right way, but I am afraid they are not what you want."

"Are they the big ones that fly mostly on June nights?" asked the Bird Woman.

"Yes," said Elnora, "great gray ones with reddish markings, pale blue-green, yellow with lavender, and red and yellow."

"What do you mean by 'red and yellow'?" asked the Bird Woman so quickly that the girl almost jumped.

"Not exactly red," explained Elnora in a trembling voice. "A reddish, yellowing brown, with canary-colored spots and gray lines on the wings."

"How many of them have you?" asked the Bird Woman in the same quick way.

"I have over one hundred specimens," said Elnora, "and at least a hundred of them are perfect."

"Perfect! How perfect?" cried the Bird Woman.

"I mean that they have whole wings and all their legs and feelers, and that no down is gone," faltered Elnora.

"Young woman, that is the rarest moth in America," said the Bird Woman solemnly. "If you have a hundred of them they are worth a hundred dollars, according to my price list. I can use all that are whole."

"What if they are not mounted right?" almost whispered Elnora.

"If they are perfect that does not make the slightest difference. I know how to soften them so that I can put them into any shape I choose. Where are they? When may I see them?" The Bird Woman's questions were eager.

"They are in the old box in the Limberlost," said Elnora. "I cannot carry many for fear of breaking them, but I can bring a few after school."

"Come here at four o'clock," said the Bird Woman, "and we will drive out with some specimen boxes and a price list and see what you have to sell. Are they your very own?"

"They are mine," replied Elnora. "No one but God knows  I have them. Mr. Duncan gave me the books and the box. He said for me to stay where I am and be brave, and my hour would come. It has! And, oh, I do need the money!"

"Could you tell me why?" asked the Bird Woman softly.

"So that I can go to high school," Elnora replied.

"What makes you so eager to go?" the Bird Woman asked.

"The swamp and all the fields around it are full of wonderful things," explained Elnora. "Every day I felt smaller and smaller and I wanted to know more and more, and soon I got desperate. As long as I could go to the Brushwood school I was happy; but just when things got to be most interesting, I could go no further with my studies in that school. I was determined to come to high school but Mother would not consent. You see, we have plenty of land but Father was drowned when I was a baby, and Mother and I cannot make money as men do. The taxes are higher every year and Mother said school is too expensive. But I could not give up the idea of getting an education and finally she bought this dress and these shoes; then I went. It was *torture!*" Elnora stopped short.

"Do you live in that beautiful cabin at the northeast end of the swamp?" asked the Bird Woman.

"Yes," replied Elnora.

"I remember the place and a story about it now. You entered the high school yesterday?"

"Yes."

"It was a humiliating day?"

"*Very!*" replied Elnora.

The Bird Woman laughed. "You cannot tell me anything I do not know about that kind of torture," she said. "I once lived in the country and entered a city school under the same conditions."

The tears began to roll down Elnora's cheeks. "Did they—?" she faltered.

"They did!" said the Bird Woman emphatically. "All of it. I am quite sure they did not miss one least little thing but I am here, able to remember it and to mingle laughter with what used to be all tears; for every day I have the work which I love and almost every day God sends someone like you to help me. What is your name?"

"Elnora Comstock," answered Elnora. "Yesterday, on the blackboard, someone changed it to *Corn*stock. For a minute I thought I should die, but I can laugh over that already."

The Bird Woman arose and kissed her. "Finish your lunch," she said, "and I will get my price list and take down a memorandum of what you think you have, so that I shall know how many boxes to prepare. And remember this: What you are lies with you. If you are lazy and accept your lot, you will be nothing and do nothing for the world. If you work intelligently, you can write your name among the only ones who live past the grave—people who write books that help, make exquisite music, carve statues, paint pictures, or serve others in various ways. Forget the calico dress and the coarse shoes. Study hard and make the most of your opportunities, and before long you will hear yesterday's tormentors boasting that they were classmates of yours."

Years afterwards, when people praised Elnora's work and were proud of having known her, she remembered the Bird Woman's words and gave thanks for the friend who helped her to find success and happiness.

Character Theme—Determination & Resourcefulness

Time to Think

1. How was Elnora's life hard?
2. Why did Elnora tell the Algebra teacher that he was beautiful?
3. Why do you think the lady in the story was called the "Bird Woman"?
4. What did the Bird Woman tell Elnora would happen if she worked intelligently?

LET MY PEOPLE GO

James Weldon Johnson

If this poem sounds different from other poems, it is because it is really a sermon. James Weldon Johnson wanted to preserve the wonderful kind of sermons preached by old-time black preachers, so he wrote several and put them in a book that he called *God's Trombones*. This poem is about Moses and the children of Israel. We are picking up the sermon right after the ten plagues when Pharaoh finally tells Moses that the Israelites may leave Egypt.

In the morning,
Oh, in the morning,
They missed the Hebrew Children.
Four hundred years,
Four hundred years
They'd held them down in Egypt land.
Held them under the driver's lash,
Working without money and without price.
And it might have been Pharaoh's wife that said:
Pharaoh—look what you've done.
You let those Hebrew Children go,
And who's going to serve us now?
Who's going to make our bricks and mortar?
Who's going to plant and plow our corn?
Who's going to get up in the chill of the morning?
And who's going to work in the blazing sun?
Pharaoh, tell me that!

And Pharaoh called his generals,
And the generals called the captains,
And the captains called the soldiers.
And they hitched up all the chariots,
Six hundred chosen chariots of war,
And twenty-four hundred horses.
And the chariots all were full of men,
With swords and shields
And shiny spears
And battle bows and arrows.

And Pharaoh and his army
Pursued the Hebrew Children
To the edge of the Red Sea.

Now, the Children of Israel, looking back,
Saw Pharaoh's army coming.
And the rumble of the chariots was like a thunder storm,
And the whirring of the wheels was like a rushing wind,
And the dust from the horses made a cloud that darked the day,
And the glittering of the spears was like lightnings in the night.

And the Children of Israel all lost faith,
The Children of Israel all lost hope;
Deep Red Sea in front of them
And Pharaoh's host behind.
And they mumbled and grumbled among themselves:
Were there no graves in Egypt?
And they wailed aloud to Moses and said:
Slavery in Egypt was better than to come
To die here in this wilderness.

But Moses said:
Stand still! Stand still!
And see the Lord's salvation.
For the Lord God of Israel
Will not forsake His people.
The Lord will break the chariots,
The Lord will break the horsemen,
He'll break great Egypt's sword and shield,
The battle bows and arrows;
This day He'll make proud Pharaoh know
Who is the God of Israel.

And Moses lifted up his rod
Over the Red Sea;
And God with a blast of His nostrils
Blew the waters apart,
And the waves rolled back and stood up in a pile,
And left a path through the middle of the sea
Dry as the sands of the desert.
And the Children of Israel all crossed over
On to the other side.

When Pharaoh saw them crossing dry,
He dashed on in behind them—
Old Pharaoh got about half way cross,
And God unlashed the waters,
And the waves rushed back together,
And Pharaoh and all his army got lost,
And all his host got drownded.
And Moses sang and Miriam danced,
And the people shouted for joy,
And God led the Hebrew Children on
Till they reached the promised land.

Listen!—Listen!
All you sons of Pharaoh.
Who do you think can hold God's people
When the Lord God Himself has said,
Let my people go?

MEET THE AUTHOR

James Weldon Johnson (1871–1938) was a well-known black poet, diplomat, and lawyer. His mother, who was a schoolteacher, trained him in music and other subjects; later he studied at Atlanta University and Columbia University and became the first black lawyer in Florida. For several years, he served as a diplomat to Venezuela and Nicaragua.

Anne of Green Gables

Lucy Maud Montgomery

Because Matthew Cuthbert needed help on his Canadian farm, he and his sister Marilla decided to take in a sturdy orphan boy who could do the chores. They were both shocked when the orphan asylum in Nova Scotia mistakenly sent them Anne Shirley, a red-headed, mischievous girl full of silly notions. The following chapters from *Anne of Green Gables* tell how Anne came to live at Green Gables.

Marilla Cuthbert Is Surprised

Marilla came briskly forward as Matthew opened the door. But when her eyes fell on the odd little figure in the stiff, ugly dress, with the long braids of red hair and the eager, luminous eyes, she stopped short in amazement.

"Matthew Cuthbert, who's that?" she said. "Where is the boy?"

"There wasn't any boy," said Matthew wretchedly. "There was only *her*."

---

gable—*the space between the two slanted
sides at the end of a roof*

asylum—*orphanage*

He nodded at the child, remembering that he had never even asked her name.

"No boy! But there *must* have been a boy," insisted Marilla. "We sent word to Mrs. Spencer to bring a boy."

"Well, she didn't. She brought *her*. I asked the station-master. And I had to bring her home. She couldn't be left there, no matter where the mistake had come in."

"Well, this is a pretty piece of business!" cried Marilla.

During this dialogue the child had remained silent, her eyes roving from one to the other, all the animation fading out of her face. Suddenly she seemed to grasp the full meaning of what had been said. Dropping her precious carpetbag she sprang forward a step and clasped her hands.

"You don't want me!" she cried. "You don't want me because I'm not a boy! I might have expected it. Nobody ever did want me. I might have known it was all too beautiful to last. I might have known nobody really did want me. Oh, what shall I do? I'm going to burst into tears!"

Burst into tears she did. Sitting down on a chair by the table, flinging her arms upon it, and burying her face in them, she proceeded to cry stormily. Marilla and Matthew looked at each other deprecatingly across the stove. Neither of them knew what to say or do. Finally Marilla stepped lamely into the breach.

"Well, well, there's no need to cry so about it."

"Yes, there *is* need!" The child raised her head quickly, revealing a tear-stained face and trembling lips. "*You* would cry, too, if you were an orphan and had come to a place you thought was going to be home and found that they didn't want you because you weren't a boy. Oh, this is the most *tragical* thing that ever happened to me!"

Something like a reluctant smile, rather rusty from long disuse, mellowed Marilla's grim expression.

---

deprecatingly—*expressing strong disapproval*
breach—*a gap*

"Well, don't cry any more. We're not going to turn you out of doors tonight. You'll have to stay here until we investigate this affair. What's your name?"

The child hesitated for a moment.

"Will you please call me Cordelia?" she said eagerly.

"*Call* you Cordelia! Is that your name?"

"No-o-o, it's not exactly my name, but I would love to be called Cordelia. It's such a perfectly elegant name."

"I don't know what on earth you mean. If Cordelia isn't your name, what is?"

"Anne Shirley," reluctantly faltered forth the owner of that name, "but oh, please do call me Cordelia. It can't matter much to you what you call me if I'm only going to be here a little while, can it? And Anne is such an unromantic name."

"Unromantic fiddlesticks!" said the unsympathetic Marilla. "Anne is a real good plain sensible name. You've no need to be ashamed of it."

"Oh, I'm not ashamed of it," explained Anne, "only I like Cordelia better. I've always imagined that my name was Cordelia—at least, I always have of late years. When I was young I used to imagine it was Geraldine, but I like Cordelia better now. But if you call me Anne please call me Anne spelled with an *e*."

"What difference does it make how it's spelled?" asked Marilla with another rusty smile as she picked up the teapot.

"Oh, it makes *such* a difference. It *looks* so much nicer. When you hear a name pronounced can't you always see it in your mind, just as if it was printed out? I can; and A-n-n looks dreadful, but A-n-n-e looks so much more distinguished. If you'll only call me Anne spelled with an *e* I shall try to reconcile myself to not being called Cordelia."

"Very well, then, Anne spelled with an *e,* can you tell us how this mistake came to be made? We sent word to Mrs. Spencer to bring us a boy. Were there no boys at the asylum?"

"Oh, yes, there was an abundance of them. But Mrs. Spencer said *distinctly* that you wanted a girl about eleven years old. And the matron said she thought I would do. You don't know how delighted I was. I couldn't sleep all last night for joy. Oh," she added reproachfully, turning to Matthew, "why didn't you tell me at the station that you didn't want me and leave me there? If I hadn't seen the White Way of Delight and the Lake of Shining Waters it wouldn't be so hard."

"What on earth does she mean?" demanded Marilla, staring at Matthew.

"She—she's just referring to some conversation we had on the road," said Matthew hastily. "I'm going out to put the mare in, Marilla. Have tea ready when I come back."

"Did Mrs. Spencer bring anybody over besides you?" continued Marilla when Matthew had gone out.

"She brought Lily Jones for herself. Lily is only five years old and she is very beautiful. She has nut-brown hair. If I was very beautiful and had nut-brown hair would you keep me?"

"No. We want a boy to help Matthew on the farm. A girl would be of no use to us. Take off your hat. I'll lay it and your bag on the hall table."

Anne took off her hat meekly. Matthew came back presently and they sat down to supper. But Anne could not eat. In vain she nibbled at the bread and butter and pecked at the crabapple preserve out of the little scalloped glass dish by her plate. She did not really make any headway at all.

"You're not eating anything," said Marilla sharply, eyeing her as if it were a serious shortcoming.

Anne sighed.

"I can't. I'm in the depths of despair. Can you eat when you are in the depths of despair?"

"I've never been in the depths of despair, so I can't say," responded Marilla.

---

matron—*the lady in charge*

"Weren't you? Well, did you ever try to *imagine* you were in the depths of despair?"

"No, I didn't."

"Then I don't think you can understand what it's like. It's a very uncomfortable feeling indeed. When you try to eat a lump comes right up in your throat and you can't swallow anything, not even if it was a chocolate caramel. I had one chocolate caramel once two years ago and it was simply delicious. I've often dreamed since then that I had a lot of chocolate caramels, but I always wake up just when I'm going to eat them. I do hope you won't be offended because I can't eat. Everything is extremely nice, but still I cannot eat."

"I guess she's tired," said Matthew, who hadn't spoken since his return from the barn. "Best put her to bed, Marilla."

Marilla had been wondering where Anne should be put to bed. She had prepared a couch in the kitchen chamber for the desired and expected boy. But, although it was neat and clean, it did not seem quite the thing to put a girl there somehow. But the spare room was out of the question for such a stray waif, so there remained only the east gable room. Marilla lighted a candle and told Anne to follow her, which Anne spiritlessly did, taking her hat and carpetbag from the hall table as she passed. The hall was fearsomely clean; the little gable chamber in which she presently found herself seemed still cleaner.

Marilla set the candle on a three-legged, three-cornered table and turned down the bedclothes.

"I suppose you have a nightgown?" she questioned.

Anne nodded.

"Yes, I have two. The matron of the asylum made them for me. They're fearfully skimpy. There is never enough to go around in an asylum, so things are always skimpy—at least in a poor asylum like ours. I hate skimpy nightdresses. But one can dream just as well in them as in lovely trailing ones, with frills around the neck, that's one consolation."

"Well, undress as quick as you can and go to bed. I'll come back in a few minutes for the candle. I daren't trust you to put it out yourself. You'd likely set the place on fire."

When Marilla had gone Anne looked around her wistfully. The white-washed walls were so painfully bare and staring that she thought they must ache over their own bareness. The floor was bare too, except for a round braided mat in the middle such as Anne had never seen before. In one corner was the bed, a high, old-fashioned one, with four dark, low-turned posts. In the other corner was the aforesaid three-cornered table adorned with a fat, red-velvet pincushion hard enough to turn the point of the most adventurous pin. Above it hung a little six-by-eight mirror. Midway between table and bed was the window, with an icy white muslin frill over it, and opposite it was the washstand. The whole apartment was of a rigidity not to be described in words, but which sent a shiver to the very marrow of Anne's bones. With a sob she hastily discarded her garments, put on

---

waif—*abandoned or orphaned child*

the skimpy nightgown, and sprang into bed where she burrowed her face downward into the pillow and pulled the clothes over her head. When Marilla came up for the light, various skimpy articles of raiment scattered most untidily over the floor and a certain tempestuous appearance of the bed were the only indications of any presence save her own.

She deliberately picked up Anne's clothes, placed them neatly on a prim yellow chair, and then, taking up the candle, went over to the bed.

"Good night," she said, a little awkwardly, but not unkindly.

Anne's white face and big eyes appeared over the bedclothes with a startling suddenness.

"How can you call it a *good* night when you know it must be the very worst night I've ever had?" she said reproachfully.

Then she dived down into invisibility again.

Marilla went slowly down to the kitchen and proceeded to wash the supper dishes.

"Well, this is a pretty kettle of fish," she said wrathfully. "This is what comes of sending word instead of going ourselves. Richard Spencer's folks have twisted that message somehow. One of us will have to drive over and see Mrs. Spencer tomorrow, that's certain. This girl will have to be sent back to the asylum."

"Yes, I suppose so," said Matthew reluctantly.

"You *suppose* so! Don't you know it?"

"Well now, she's a real nice little thing, Marilla. It's kind of a pity to send her back when she's so set on staying here."

"Matthew Cuthbert, you don't mean to say you think we ought to keep her!"

Marilla's astonishment could not have been greater if Matthew had expressed a predilection for standing on his head.

"Well now, no, I suppose not—not exactly," stammered Matthew, uncomfortably driven into a corner for his precise meaning. "I suppose—we could hardly be expected to keep her."

---

tempestuous—*resembling a storm*   predilection—*a preference*

198

"I should say not. What good would she be to us?"

"We might be some good to her," said Matthew suddenly and unexpectedly.

"Matthew Cuthbert, I believe that child has bewitched you! I can see as plain as plain that you want to keep her."

"Well now, she's a real interesting little thing," persisted Matthew. "You should have heard her talk coming from the station."

"Oh, she can talk fast enough. I saw that at once. It's nothing in her favor, either. I don't like children who have so much to say. I don't want an orphan girl and if I did she isn't the style I'd pick out. There's something I don't understand about her. No, she's got to be dispatched straightway back to where she came from."

"I could hire a French boy to help me," said Matthew, "and she'd be company for you."

"I'm not suffering for company," said Marilla shortly. "And I'm not going to keep her."

"Well now, it's just as you say, of course, Marilla," said Matthew, rising and putting his pipe away. "I'm going to bed."

To bed went Matthew, and to bed, when she had put her dishes away, went Marilla, frowning most resolutely. And upstairs, in the east gable, a lonely, heart-hungry, friendless child cried herself to sleep.

Morning at Green Gables

It was broad daylight when Anne awoke and sat up in bed, staring confusedly at the window through which a flood of cheery sunshine was pouring and outside of which something white and feathery waved across glimpses of blue sky.

For a moment she could not remember where she was. First came a delightful thrill, as of something very pleasant; then a horrible remembrance. This was Green Gables and they didn't want her because she wasn't a boy!

But it was morning and, yes, it was a cherry tree in full bloom outside her window. With a bound she was out of bed and across

the floor. She pushed up the sash—it went up stiffly and creakily, as if it hadn't been opened for a long time, which was the case; and it stuck so tight that nothing was needed to hold it up.

Anne dropped on her knees and gazed out into the June morning, her eyes glistening with delight. Oh, wasn't it beautiful? Wasn't it a lovely place? Suppose she wasn't really going to stay here! She would imagine she was. There was scope for imagination here.

A huge cherry tree grew outside, so close that its boughs tapped against the house, and it was so thick-set with blossoms that hardly a leaf was to be seen. On both sides of the house was a big orchard, one of apple trees and one of cherry trees, also showered over with blossoms; and their grass was all sprinkled with dandelions. In the garden below were lilac trees purple with flowers, and their dizzily sweet fragrance drifted up to the window on the morning wind.

Below the garden a green field lush with clover sloped down to the hollow where the brook ran and where scores of white birches grew, upspringing airily out of an undergrowth suggestive of delightful possibilities in ferns and mosses and woodsy things generally. Beyond it was a hill, green and feathery with spruce and fir; there was a gap in it where the gray gable end of the little house she had seen from the other side of the Lake of Shining Waters was visible.

Off to the left were the big barns and beyond them, away down over green, low-sloping fields, was a sparkling blue glimpse of sea.

Anne's beauty-loving eyes lingered on it all, taking everything greedily in. She had looked on so many unlovely places in her life, poor child; but this was as lovely as anything she had ever dreamed.

She knelt there, lost to everything but the loveliness around her, until she was startled by a hand on her shoulder. Marilla had come in unheard by the small dreamer.

"It's time you were dressed," she said curtly.

Marilla really did not know how to talk to the child, and her uncomfortable ignorance made her crisp and curt when she did not mean to be.

Anne stood up and drew a long breath.

"Oh, isn't it wonderful?" she said waving her hand comprehensively at the good world outside.

"It's a big tree," said Marilla, "and it blooms great, but the fruit don't amount to much never—small and wormy."

"Oh, I don't mean just the tree; of course it's lovely—yes, it's *radiantly* lovely—it blooms as if it meant it—but I meant everything, the garden and the orchard and the brook and the woods, the whole big dear world. Don't you feel as if you just loved the world on a morning like this? And I can hear the brook laughing all the way up here. Have you ever noticed what cheerful things brooks are? They're always laughing. Even in wintertime I've heard them under the ice. I'm so glad there's a brook near Green Gables. Perhaps you think it doesn't make any difference to me when you're not going to keep me, but it does. I shall always like to remember that there is a brook at Green Gables even if I never see it again. If there wasn't a brook I'd be *haunted* by the uncomfortable feeling that there ought to be one. I'm not in the depths of despair this morning. I never can be in the morning. Isn't it a splendid thing that there are mornings? But I feel very sad. I've just been imagining that it was really me you wanted after all and that I was to stay here for ever and ever. It was a great comfort while it lasted. But the worst of imagining things is that the time comes when you have to stop and that hurts."

"You'd better get dressed and come downstairs and never mind your imaginings," said Marilla as soon as she could get a word in edgewise. "Breakfast is waiting. Wash your face and comb your hair. Leave the window up and turn your bedclothes back over the foot of the bed. Be as smart as you can."

Anne could evidently be smart to some purpose for she was downstairs in ten minutes' time, with her clothes neatly on, her hair brushed and braided, her face washed, and a comfortable consciousness pervading her soul that she had fulfilled all Marilla's requirements. As a matter of fact, however, she had forgotten to turn back the bedclothes.

"I'm pretty hungry this morning," she announced, as she slipped into the chair Marilla placed for her. "The world doesn't seem such a howling wilderness as it did last night. I'm so glad it's a sunshiny morning. But I like rainy mornings real well, too. All sorts of mornings are interesting, don't you think? You don't know what's going to happen through the day, and there's so much scope for imagination. But I'm glad it's not rainy today because it's easier to be cheerful and bear up under affliction on a sunshiny day. I feel that I have a good deal to bear up under. It's all very well to read about sorrows and imagine yourself living through them heroically, but it's not so nice when you really come to have them, is it?"

---

smart—*quick in movement*

"For pity's sake hold your tongue," said Marilla. "You talk entirely too much for a little girl."

Thereupon Anne held her tongue so obediently and thoroughly that her continued silence made Marilla rather nervous, as if in the presence of something not exactly natural. Matthew also held his tongue—but this at least was natural—so that the meal was a very silent one.

As it progressed Anne became more and more abstracted, eating mechanically, with her big eyes fixed unswervingly and unseeingly on the sky outside the window. This made Marilla more nervous than ever; she had an uncomfortable feeling that while this odd child's body might be there at the table her spirit was far away in some remote airy cloudland, borne aloft on the wings of imagination. Who would want such a child about the place?

Yet Matthew wished to keep her, of all unaccountable things! Marilla felt that he wanted it just as much this morning as he had the night before, and that he would go on wanting it. That was Matthew's way—take a whim into his head and cling to it with the most amazing silent persistency—a persistency ten times more potent and effectual in its very silence than if he had talked it out.

When the meal was ended Anne came out of her reverie and offered to wash the dishes.

"Can you wash dishes right?" asked Marilla distrustfully.

"Pretty well. I'm better at looking after children, though. I've had so much experience at that. It's such a pity you haven't any here for me to look after."

"I don't feel as if I wanted any more children to look after than I've got at present. *You're* problem enough in all conscience. What's to be done with you I don't know. Matthew is a most ridiculous man."

---

abstracted—*lost in thought*
whim—*a sudden idea*

reverie—*dreamy thinking of*
pleasant things

"I think he's lovely," said Anne reproachfully. "He is so very sympathetic. He didn't mind how much I talked—he seemed to like it. I felt that he was a kindred spirit as soon as ever I saw him."

"You're both strange enough, if that's what you mean by kindred spirits," said Marilla, with a sniff. "Yes, you may wash the dishes. Take plenty of hot water, and be sure you dry them well. I've got enough to attend to this morning, for I'll have to drive over to White Sands in the afternoon and see Mrs. Spencer. You'll come with me and we'll settle what's to be done with you. After you've finished the dishes go upstairs and make your bed."

Anne washed the dishes deftly enough, as Marilla, who kept a sharp eye on the process, discerned. Later on she made her bed less successfully, for she had never learned the art of wrestling with a feather tick. But it was done somehow and smoothed down; and then Marilla, to get rid of her, told her she might go out of doors and amuse herself until dinnertime.

Anne flew to the door, face alight, eyes glowing. On the very threshold she stopped short, wheeled about, came back, and sat down by the table, light and glow as effectually blotted out as if someone had clapped an extinguisher on her.

"What's the matter now?" demanded Marilla.

"I don't dare go out," said Anne, in the tone of a martyr relinquishing all earthly joys. "If I can't stay here there is no use in my loving Green Gables. And if I go out there and get acquainted with all those trees and flowers and the orchard and the brook, I'll not be able to help loving it. It's hard enough now, so I won't make it any harder. I want to go out so much—everything seems to be calling to me, 'Anne, Anne, come out to us. Anne, Anne, we want a playmate'—but it's better not. There is no use in loving things if you have to be torn from them, is there? And it's *so* hard to keep from loving things, isn't it? That was why

---

kindred spirit—*one who naturally understands another's thoughts and feelings*
tick—*mattress*

extinguisher—*a small metal cone used for putting out candles*

I was so glad when I thought I was going to live here. I thought I'd have so many things to love and nothing to hinder me. But that brief dream is over. I am resigned to my fate now, so I don't think I'll go out for fear I'll get unresigned again. What is the name of that geranium on the windowsill, please?"

"That's the apple-scented geranium."

"Oh, I don't mean that sort of a name. I mean just a name you gave it yourself. Didn't you give it a name? May I give it one then? May I call it—let me see—Bonny would do—may I call it Bonny while I'm here? Oh, do let me!"

"Goodness, I don't care. But where on earth is the sense of naming a geranium?"

"Oh, I like things to have handles even if they are only geraniums. It makes them seem more like people. How do you know but that it hurts a geranium's feelings just to be called a geranium and nothing else? You wouldn't like to be called nothing but a woman all the time. Yes, I shall call it Bonny. I named that cherry tree outside my bedroom window this morning. I called it Snow Queen because it was so white. Of course, it won't always be in blossom, but one can imagine that it is, can't one?"

"I never in all my life saw or heard anything to equal her," muttered Marilla, beating a retreat down cellar after potatoes. "She *is* kind of interesting, as Matthew says. I can feel already that I'm wondering what on earth she'll say next. She'll be casting a spell over me too. She's cast it over Matthew. That look he gave me when he went out said everything he said or hinted last night over again. I wish he was like other men and would talk things out. A body would answer back then and argue him into reason. But what's to be done with a man who just *looks*?"

Anne had relapsed into reverie, with her chin in her hands and her eyes on the sky, when Marilla returned from her cellar pilgrimage. There Marilla left her until the early dinner was on the table.

---

pilgrimage—*a long journey or search*

"I suppose I can have the mare and buggy this afternoon, Matthew?" said Marilla.

Matthew nodded and looked wistfully at Anne. Marilla intercepted the look and said grimly:

"I'm going to drive over to White Sands and settle this thing. I'll take Anne with me and Mrs. Spencer will probably make arrangements to send her back to Nova Scotia at once. I'll set your tea out for you and I'll be home in time to milk the cows."

Still Matthew said nothing and Marilla had a sense of having wasted words and breath. There is nothing more aggravating than a man who won't talk back—unless it is a woman who won't.

Matthew hitched the sorrel into the buggy in due time and Marilla and Anne set off. Matthew opened the yard gate for them, and as they drove slowly through, he said, to nobody in particular as it seemed:

"Little Jerry Buote from the Creek was here this morning, and I told him I guessed I'd hire him for the summer."

Marilla made no reply, but she hit the unlucky sorrel such a vicious clip with the whip that the fat mare, unused to such treatment, whizzed indignantly down the lane at an alarming pace. Marilla looked back once as the buggy bounced along and saw that aggravating Matthew leaning over the gate, looking wistfully after them.

Marilla Makes up Her Mind

Get there they did, however, in due season. Mrs. Spencer lived in a big yellow house at White Sands Cove, and she came to the door with surprise and welcome mingled on her benevolent face.

"Dear, dear," she exclaimed, "you're the last folks I was looking for today, but I'm real glad to see you. You'll put your horse in? And how are you, Anne?"

"I'm as well as can be expected, thank you," said Anne smilelessly. A blight seemed to have descended on her.

"I suppose we'll stay a little while to rest the mare," said Marilla, "but I promised Matthew I'd be home early. The fact is, Mrs. Spencer, there's been a mistake somewhere, and I've come over to see where it is. We sent word, Matthew and I, for you to bring us a boy from the asylum. We told your brother Robert to tell you we wanted a boy ten or eleven years old."

"Marilla Cuthbert, you don't say so!" said Mrs. Spencer in distress. "Why, Robert sent the word down by his daughter Nancy and she said you wanted a girl—didn't she, Flora Jane?" appealing to her daughter, who had come out to the steps.

"She certainly did, Miss Cuthbert," corroborated Flora Jane earnestly.

"I'm dreadful sorry," said Mrs. Spencer. "It is too bad; but it certainly wasn't my fault, you see, Miss Cuthbert. I did the best I could and I thought I was following your instructions. Nancy is a terrible flighty thing. I've often had to scold her well for her heedlessness."

"It was our own fault," said Marilla resignedly. "We should have come to you ourselves and not left an important message to be passed along by word of mouth in that fashion. Anyhow, the mistake has been made and the only thing to do now is to set it right. Can we send the child back to the asylum? I suppose they'll take her back, won't they?"

corroborated—*gave confirmation*

"I suppose so," said Mrs. Spencer thoughtfully, "but I don't think it will be necessary to send her back. Mrs. Peter Blewett was up here yesterday, and she was saying to me how much she wished she'd sent by me for a little girl to help her. Mrs. Peter has a large family, you know, and she finds it hard to get help. Anne will be the very girl for her. I call it positively providential."

Marilla did not look as if she thought Providence had much to do with the matter. Here was an unexpectedly good chance to get this unwelcome orphan off her hands, and she did not even feel grateful for it.

She knew Mrs. Peter Blewett only by sight as a small, shrewish-faced woman without an ounce of superfluous flesh on her bones. But she had heard of her. "A terrible worker and driver," Mrs. Peter was said to be; and discharged servant girls told fearsome tales of her temper and stinginess, and her family of pert, quarrelsome children. Marilla felt a qualm of conscience at the thought of handing Anne over to her tender mercies.

"Well, I'll go in and we'll talk the matter over," she said.

"And if there isn't Mrs. Peter coming up the lane this blessed minute!" exclaimed Mrs. Spencer, bustling her guests through the hall into the parlor, where a deadly chill struck on them as if the air had been strained so long through dark-green, closely drawn blinds that it had lost every particle of warmth it had ever possessed. "That is real lucky, for we can settle the matter right away. Take the armchair, Miss Cuthbert. Anne, you sit there on the ottoman and don't wriggle. Let me take your hats. Flora Jane, go out and put the kettle on. Good afternoon, Mrs. Blewett. We were just saying how fortunate it was you happened along. Let me introduce you two ladies. Mrs. Blewett, Miss Cuthbert. Please excuse me for just a moment. I forgot to tell Flora Jane to take the buns out of the oven."

---

providential—*from God*   **superfluous**—*extra*

208

Mrs. Spencer whisked away, after pulling up the blinds. Anne, sitting mutely on the ottoman, with her hands clasped tightly in her lap, stared at Mrs. Blewett as one fascinated. Was she to be given into the keeping of this sharp-faced, sharp-eyed woman? She felt a lump coming up in her throat and her eyes smarted painfully. She was beginning to be afraid she couldn't keep the tears back when Mrs. Spencer returned, flushed and beaming, quite capable of taking any and every difficulty, physical, mental, or spiritual, into consideration and settling it out of hand.

"It seems there's been a mistake about this little girl, Mrs. Blewett," she said. "I was under the impression that Mr. and Miss Cuthbert wanted a little girl to adopt. I was certainly told so. But it seems it was a boy they wanted. So if you're still of the same mind you were yesterday, I think she'll be just the thing for you."

Mrs. Blewett darted her eyes over Anne from head to foot.

"How old are you and what's your name?" she demanded.

"Anne Shirley," faltered the shrinking child, not daring to make any stipulations regarding the spelling thereof, "and I'm eleven years old."

"Humph! You don't look as if there was much to you. But you're wiry. I don't know but the wiry ones are the best after all. Well, if I take you you'll have to be a good girl, you know—good and smart and respectful. I'll expect you to earn your keep, and no mistake about that. Yes, I suppose I might as well take her off your hands, Miss Cuthbert. The baby's awful fractious, and I'm clean worn out attending to him. If you like I can take her right home now."

Marilla looked at Anne and softened at sight of the child's pale face with its look of mute misery—the misery of a helpless little creature who finds itself once more caught in the trap from which it had escaped. Marilla felt an uncomfortable conviction that, if she denied the appeal of that look, it would haunt her to her dying day. Moreover, she did not fancy Mrs. Blewett. To hand a sensitive, "high-strung" child over to such a woman! No, she could not take the responsibility of doing that!

"Well, I don't know," she said slowly. "I didn't say that Matthew and I had absolutely decided that we wouldn't keep her. In fact, I may say that Matthew is disposed to keep her. I just came over to find out how the mistake had occurred. I think I'd better take her home again and talk it over with Matthew. I feel that I oughtn't to decide on anything without consulting him. If we make up our mind not to keep her we'll bring or send her over to you tomorrow night. If we don't, you may know that she is going to stay with us. Will that suit you, Mrs. Blewett?"

"I suppose it'll have to," said Mrs. Blewett ungraciously.

During Marilla's speech a sunrise had been dawning on Anne's face. First the look of despair faded out; then came a faint flush of hope; her eyes grew deep and bright as morning stars. The child

---

stipulations—*restrictions*
fractious—*hard to manage*

disposed—*settled about a matter*

was quite transfigured; and, a moment later, when Mrs. Spencer and Mrs. Blewett went out in quest of a recipe the latter had come to borrow, she sprang up and flew across the room to Marilla.

"Oh, Miss Cuthbert, did you really say that perhaps you would let me stay at Green Gables?" she said, in a breathless whisper, as if speaking aloud might shatter the glorious possibility. "Did you really say it? Or did I only imagine that you did?"

"I think you'd better learn to control that imagination of yours, Anne, if you can't distinguish between what is real and what isn't," said Marilla crossly. "Yes, you did hear me say just that and no more. It isn't decided yet and perhaps we will conclude to let Mrs. Blewett take you after all. She certainly needs you much more than I do."

"I'd rather go back to the asylum than go to live with her," said Anne passionately. "She looks exactly like a—like a gimlet."

Marilla smothered a smile under the conviction that Anne must be reproved for such a speech.

"A little girl like you should be ashamed of talking so about a lady and a stranger," she said severely. "Go back and sit down quietly and hold your tongue and behave as a good girl should."

"I'll try to do and be anything you want me, if you'll only keep me," said Anne returning meekly to her ottoman.

When they arrived back at Green Gables that evening Matthew met them in the lane. Marilla from afar had noted him prowling along it and guessed his motive. She was prepared for the relief she read in his face when he saw that she had at least brought Anne back with her. But she said nothing to him, relative to the affair, until they were both out in the yard behind the barn milking the cows. Then she briefly told him Anne's history and the result of the interview with Mrs. Spencer.

"I wouldn't give a dog I liked to that Blewett woman," said Matthew, with unusual vim.

---

gimlet—*a screwlike tool used to bore holes*   vim—*energy*

"I don't fancy her style myself," admitted Marilla, "but it's that or keeping her ourselves, Matthew. And, since you seem to want her, I suppose I'm willing—or have to be. I've been thinking over the idea until I've got kind of used to it. It seems a sort of duty. I've never brought up a child, especially a girl, and I dare say I'll make a terrible mess of it. But I'll do my best. So far as I'm concerned, Matthew, she may stay."

Matthew's shy face was a glow of delight.

"Well now, I reckoned you'd come to see it in that light, Marilla," he said. "She's such an interesting little thing."

"It'd be more to the point if you could say she was a useful little thing," retorted Marilla, "but I'll make it my business to see she's trained to be that. And mind, Matthew, you're not to go interfering with my methods. Perhaps an old maid doesn't know much about bringing up a child, but I guess she knows more than an old bachelor. So you just leave me to manage her. When I fail it'll be time enough to put your oar in."

"There, there, Marilla, you can have your own way," said Matthew reassuringly. "Only be as good and kind to her as you can be without spoiling her. I kind of think she's one of the sort you can do anything with if you only get her to love you."

Marilla sniffed, to express her contempt for Matthew's opinions concerning anything feminine, and walked off to the dairy with the pails.

"I won't tell her tonight that she can stay," she reflected, as she strained the milk into the creamers. "She'd be so excited that she wouldn't sleep a wink. Marilla Cuthbert, you're fairly in for it. Did you ever suppose you'd see the day when you'd be adopting an orphan girl? It's surprising enough; but not so surprising as that Matthew should be at the bottom of it, him that always seemed to have such a mortal dread of little girls. Anyhow, we've decided on the experiment and goodness only knows what will come of it."

Character Theme—Compassion & Responsibility

Time to Think

1. From what country does this story come?
2. Why didn't Marilla want Anne?
3. Anne was not hungry for food. Still, the author says that she was "heart-hungry." Can you explain that?
4. Why was Marilla sharp with Anne?
5. How did Marilla change in her attitude toward Anne?
6. What finally made Marilla decide to let Anne stay at Green Gables?
7. Do you think Anne would have been a good friend? Why?

MEET THE AUTHOR

L. M. Montgomery was born on Prince Edward Island in Canada, the setting of her "Anne" books. As a child, she lived with her grandmother in an old farmhouse, writing poems and stories. One day Miss Montgomery read an old faded newspaper clipping which said, "Elderly couple apply to Orphan Asylum for boy. By mistake girl is sent. . . ." In Miss Montgomery's vivid imagination, a picture of that elderly couple and the orphan girl developed. She began to write down what she imagined, and the result was the book *Anne of Green Gables.*

After *Anne of Green Gables* was published, Miss Montgomery received thousands of letters from Canadian and American young people asking for more "Anne" stories. You might want to read the entire *Anne of Green Gables* novel and then *Anne of Avonlea, Anne of the Island, Anne of Windy Poplars, Anne's House of Dreams,* and other "Anne" books by L. M. Montgomery.

Beloved Friend of Little Waifs

Anna Talbott McPherson
(adapted)

Children, children everywhere. Hordes of them. George Müller watched them pour down the steps into the dining hall for their supper. Flaxen-haired, golden-haired, brown-haired, black-haired. Boys with locks cropped closely. Girls with saucy pigtails or jaunty ringlets bobbing.

What potential was represented here! What responsibilities! Sometimes the thought almost staggered the man who watched. And what scamps these waifs could be when they forgot themselves. But how he loved them—every one of them.

Müller was reminded that in four more houses children were streaming down steps into dining halls—more than 2,000 of these homeless babes looking to him as to a father for food, for clothing, for shelter, for love.

On and on they came, bowing to him as they passed, quietly taking their places at the tables. Things were as they always had been, or at least they looked that way. The little ones never dreamed that Father Müller, watching, smiling, did not have great bakeries full of bread for them to eat, great dairies full of milk for them to drink.

That night every orphan's mug was full of milk, just as each orphan had taken for granted it would be. No little one knew that not a drop remained for breakfast on the next day, that not a penny was in hand to buy a mugful more.

What would he do—this man who had taken so many homeless ones under his wings? Why, he would do as he had done hundreds of times before—go to his knees and tell his

---

hordes—*crowds*   flaxen—*blond*
Müller (my$\overline{oo}$'lər)   jaunty—*bouncy*

heavenly Father that His children needed milk. Just this simply did George Müller and his staff of workers ask. Just this simply did they believe.

The next morning dawned, finding that George Müller had already been in prayer for two whole hours—not anxiously worrying about the gallons and gallons of milk needed for breakfast but already thanking God that the milk was on its way!

Again the hordes of children trooped down the stairs. Bright-eyed they were, zestful, laughing. No milk was in their mugs, but there would be some. They were sure of that. Now their heads were bowed and Mr. Müller simply, gratefully thanked the kind heavenly Father of orphans for daily bread— and for milk!

The prayer ended; a loud knock shook the great oaken door at the end of the spacious kitchen. The man of God threw it wide, and there stood none other than the milkman himself!

"Mr. Müller," boomed the dairyman's voice, "just don't know how it happened, but my wagon broke down out here. Wheel smashed to pieces. Can't get to town with my milk. Don't want to let it go to waste. Come, help me carry it in, and it's all yours. For nothing too!"

Before the hungry urchins knew just what it was all about, milk—sweet, delicious, creamy—had filled the last waiting mug.

Instances like this one were not uncommon in George Müller's daily life as the "father" of orphans. According to his own testimony, not simply scores of times but literally hundreds of times he had been absolutely destitute of food and money when the moment came to serve a meal to his great family. "Yet," said he, "in all these years, never on a single occasion has God permitted those orphans to go without a meal at the time when it was due. In order to provide for them, He has . . . sent money from all the ends of the earth, awakened people out of their sleep, sent people out of their way, has done seemingly almost everything that could be done to make sure that those who were trusting Him should not lack for any good thing."

Always when needs were pressing, Mr. Müller would call the staff together for prayer. And often, when getting off their knees, they would see dray wagons backing up to the kitchen door, loaded with buns, bread, apples, cakes, potatoes, boxes of soap, sacks of peas, haunches of venison, rabbits and pheasants, and every other kind of food.

Once a woman gave Mr. Müller her jewels to be exchanged for money for the orphanages. Her gift came at the time of such pressing need and Mr. Müller's joy was so full that before he sold the diamond ring, he wrote with it upon the windowpane of his own room that precious name and title of the Lord, "Jehovah Jireh." After that—whenever, in deep poverty, he let his eyes fall on those words—he thankfully remembered that "the Lord will provide."

A man once sent a gold watch to the orphanage with a note saying, "A pilgrim does not want such a watch as this to make him happy: one of an inferior kind will do to show how swiftly

urchins—*small children*
destitute—*lacking necessary things*
dray wagons—*large, heavy carts without sides*

Jehovah Jireh (jī′rə)—*Hebrew word meaning "the Lord will provide"*

time flies, and how fast he is hastening on to that Canaan where time will be no more."

How did this orphanage work, so blessed of God, have its beginning?

George Müller was converted at the age of twenty while he was a student at Halle. At first he wanted to be a missionary, but by various circumstances was prevented from carrying out this plan. Instead, he served in small churches. Upon an invitation from Henry Craik to go to Bristol, England, and help him in church work there, Mr. Müller and his wife left their native Prussia and for eight years ministered to a growing congregation. During this time they lived by faith in the promises of God alone.

While Mr. Müller was serving in Bristol, there came into his hand a biography of August H. Francke through whom God, for thirty years, had supplied the needs of nearly 2,000 orphans.

Mr. Müller looked about him. Orphans swarmed everywhere in Bristol. These urchins—dirty, unkempt, hungry, victims of all the evil influences of the city—touched Mr. Müller's heart. God had helped Francke; God would help him.

He gathered the waifs about him. At eight o'clock each morning he fed them a little breakfast, and then for an hour and a half he taught them out of the Scriptures. He soon found himself feeding from thirty to forty such children.

Out of this beginning sprang the Scriptural Knowledge Institution, the object of which was to assist day schools and Sunday schools, to distribute Bibles, and to aid missionary efforts. Out of this beginning sprang also Mr. Müller's orphan houses. The first one, at No. 6 Wilson Street, was opened on April 21, 1836. Some months later the second house opened. A third came into being in October, 1837. When Mr. Müller was about to rent a house on the same street for a fourth children's

---

Halle (hä′lə)—*a city in Prussia (modern Germany)*   unkempt—*untidy* home, kind but firm objections were received from citizens in the neighborhood. While Mr. Müller never before had considered building houses for his orphans, this circumstance led him to lay the matter before the Lord. He decided that if sufficient extra money came into his hands, he would take it as an assurance that God wanted him to build. Otherwise, he would be content to rent. After a seven-week test of faith and patience, during which Mr. Müller said he had a sweet satisfaction in the greatness of the difficulties, he received $5,000 for his orphan work. That was the largest gift he had received since he took in his first orphan almost nine years before.

The first orphan house on Ashley Down was ready for occupancy June 18, 1849. By 1870, five of these houses had been erected. They were roomy stone buildings, accommodating more than 2,000 little ones. In all, Müller spent $4,944,145 in orphanages which housed a total of 10,024 orphans. After all five houses were put into operation, Müller's daily expenses for orphan needs was over $500.

In addition to the orphanages, the Scriptural Knowledge Institution, which required unbelievable amounts of money, was also dependent upon Mr. Müller. During the sixty-three years in which he was the superintendent, almost 2,000,000 Bibles and portions of Scripture and 111,000,000 tracts in many different languages were distributed in almost all parts of the world. In his Christian day schools, a total of 121,683 pupils were instructed not only in regular school subjects but also in the ways of God. He aided 115 missionary laborers at a total cost of over $1,300,000.

One might well ask, "How was Mr. Müller able to lay his hands on so great an amount of money?" According to his own testimony, God was his only resource for the seven and a half million dollars that passed through his hands. He never looked to man for support, never depended upon a regular income, never went into debt. He called God his rich treasurer and never doubted that God who had raised up the work through him would sustain it. Mr. Müller realized that God would not fail him since his primary object in carrying on the work was that people see that "God is still the living God, and that . . . He listens to the prayers of His children and helps those who trust in Him."

Mr. Müller's faith was tested almost daily. One day, however, while reading his Bible on his knees, as was his custom, his soul was deeply moved by the phrase, "a Father of the fatherless." Thereafter he reminded the Lord of this. "Thou art their Father," he would say. "Thou hast pledged Thyself, as it were, to provide for them." Thus, he cast the burden of caring for all the orphans on his heavenly Father and his faith stood strong when all the tests came, "In 1,000 trials it is not 500 of them that work for the believer's good, but 999 of them and one beside."

Though Mr. Müller had an itemized record of over 50,000 answered prayers, they never lost their novelty or charm for him. Once, at a time of sore need when the Lord sent $1,500 in one sum, the man of God could scarcely contain his triumphant joy. He walked up and down his room for a long time, his heart overflowing, his eyes filled with tears too, his being filled with laughter and his voice with song, while he gave himself afresh to the faithful Master he served.

Many demands were made on Müller's faith aside from financial ones. Once a serious leak in the boiler of the furnace required putting out the fires for repairs near the end of a cold November. How were 300 children and babies in this orphanage house to be kept warm?

Müller prayed.

A day or so before the fires were to be extinguished, a cutting north wind set in. But the man of God was not worried. "Lord," he appealed to the Almighty, "these are Thy orphans; be

---

novelty—*newness*

pleased to change this north wind into a south wind, and give the workmen a mind to work that the job may be speedily done."

The evening before the repairs actually began the frigid blast was still blowing. But on that day a south wind blew, and the weather was so mild that no fire was needed. Furthermore, the men volunteered to work all night, so that before the weather chilled again, the repairs were completed.

At seventy years of age, Mr. Müller launched upon his missionary tours which numbered seventeen in all. By the time he was eighty-three he had traveled over 200,000 miles in forty-two countries and had spoken five or six thousand times. These journeys had no connection with gaining money for the orphanages, yet God graciously supplied the needs of the work at Bristol, guided and guarded it so that it suffered nothing from Mr. Müller's absence.

On a voyage from Liverpool to Quebec, the fog was so heavy that very slow progress was being made. Mr. Müller went to the captain.

"Captain," he said, "I have come to tell you I must be in Quebec Saturday afternoon."

"That is impossible," returned the captain, shaking his head.

"Very well, then," spoke Müller calmly, "if your ship cannot take me, God will find some other way. I have never broken an engagement in fifty-seven years." Then, after a moment, "Let us go down into the chart room and pray."

The captain eyed Müller as though wondering from what lunatic asylum this absurd old man could have come.

"Do you know how dense this fog is, Mr. Müller?" the captain asked.

"No," Müller replied, "my eye is not on the density of the fog but on the living God who controls every circumstance of my life."

The good man knelt down and prayed one of the simplest of prayers. When he finished, the captain fidgeted and cleared his throat.

"No," Mr. Müller said kindly, placing his hand on the captain's shoulder, "do not pray. First, you do not believe He will answer. And, second, I believe He has, and there is no need whatever for you to pray about it."

The captain looked at his passenger mystified.

"I have known my Lord for fifty-seven years," Mr. Müller went on, "and there has never been a single day that I have failed to get audience with the King. If you will get up now and open the door, you will find the fog gone."

The captain did as Mr. Müller suggested. He opened the door upon a clear, fogless scene. George Müller was in Quebec for his engagement on Saturday afternoon.

On one of his return trips to Liverpool from Quebec, Müller stepped up to the express agent at the dock. "Has a deck chair come from New York for me?" he inquired.

"No," returned the agent. Then, looking at his watch, "and it cannot possibly come now in time for the steamer."

Major D. W. Whittle, a friend of Mr. Müller, was standing by. "I'll show you where I purchased my chair," he offered. "We have only a few moments left. Let's go get one quickly."

"No, my brother," Mr. Müller objected. "Our heavenly Father will send the chair from New York. It is one used by Mrs. Müller. I wrote ten days ago to a brother who promised to see it forwarded here last week. He has not been prompt, as I would have desired, but I am sure our heavenly Father will send the chair. Mrs. Müller is very sick on the sea and has particularly desired to have this same chair, and not finding it here yesterday, we have made special prayer that our heavenly Father would be pleased to provide it for us, and we will trust Him to do so."

Major Whittle watched the man of God go peacefully on board the ship. *I wonder if he is not carrying his faith principles too far,* he thought to himself. *Here he is, running the risk of causing Mrs. Müller to make the trip without a chair, when for a couple of dollars he could be sure of having one.*

Having been detained in the express office ten minutes after Müller left, the major was hurrying to the wharf when a team drove up the street pulling a dray. Perched on the very top of the load which had just arrived from New York was a chair—Müller's chair. It was given to the major who then gave it to Müller. The good man received it just as the boat was leaving the dock. With a look of unutterable gratitude, he removed his hat, reverently folded his hands upon the chair, and gave thanks to his Father in Heaven who had not forgotten.

George Müller prayed for the conversion of souls as well as for material needs. It took sixty-two years of his praying for two men before they finally yielded to God and even then Mr. Müller did not live to see the transformation, but his faith had grasped the answer at the outset. "No, they are not converted yet," he would say, "but they will be!"

Asked what the secret of his service was, Mr. Müller—tall, stately—bent so low he almost touched the floor. "There was a day when I died," he said, speaking with deliberation in a noticeable German accent, "utterly died to George Müller, to his opinions, preferences, tastes, and will; died to the world, its approval or censure; died to the approval or blame of even my brethren and friends. Since then I have studied to show myself approved only unto God . . . I love holiness; yes, I love holiness more and more."

George Müller, that stalwart of the faith who, on the night before his death, first confessed to feeling weak and weary, filled his ninety-two years to the brim in trying to bring glory to God by showing to the whole world that "yet in these days God listens to prayer and is the same in power and love as ever." Said Mr. Müller, "Caring for the children is the mere instrumentality to this end." Yet into this ministry he invested his tenderest concern and prayers. He sacrificed that they might be fed and clothed and sheltered and saved. And it is because of this burning passion in George Müller's soul that he is remembered as the beloved friend of thousands of friendless waifs.

---

censure—*criticism*
instrumentality—*a way of getting something done*

Character Theme—Faith

Time to Think

1. Explain how George Müller was able to care for 2,000 orphans.
2. Where were Mr. Müller's orphanages?
3. How does this story of George Müller inspire you?
4. What did Mr. Müller mean when he said, "There was a day when I died"?

Dr. Joseph Lister

Iris Noble

The English physician Joseph Lister was the Father of Antiseptic Surgery. When Lister started his medical studies, a very large percentage of people who had operations died of gangrene. This was not because surgeons lacked skill but because no one knew that infection is caused by germs. In 1865 Lister opened a new era for surgery when he demonstrated in the ward of a hospital in Glasgow, Scotland, that infection can be controlled.

In the spring of 1865, a professor of chemistry stopped by Dr. Joseph Lister's office one afternoon. He was carrying a magazine in his hand.

"Mr. Lister," he said, "I've just come across something strange in this publication of the French Academy of Sciences. Will you tell me what you think about it?"

That evening the doctor sat in his favorite chair in his study. The evening was cold, and there was a good, bright fire warming his outstretched legs. Nearby, Agnes, his wife, was curled up on the sofa, not reading tonight, as she usually was, but knitting a sweater for her husband.

"I'd like to measure your sleeve length," she said to him after a while. When there was no answer from her usually polite Joseph, she looked over at him, startled.

There was a strange expression on his face—half fierce, eager hope; half awed, fearful wonder.

"Joseph, dear?" she said softly.

He raised eyes that seemed blind to her and to the room about him. On his face was a look of great excitement.

"Aggie, Aggie, the most wonderful thing! A chemist in France named Louis Pasteur has discovered what causes fermentation and putrefaction in wine and milk! Do you see what this means? Pasteur did endless experiments with alcohol and milk, and he found that there are living organisms—*living things!*—that get inside a liquid and make changes in it."

Agnes felt that she was being stupid. "But if they are living, why haven't others seen them? What does he call them?"

"Others have seen them. A man named Leeuwenhoek saw them more than a hundred years ago under a microscope. Other scientists who saw them later called them microbes."

"Microbes! But I've seen that word before!"

"Of course you have. And so have I and other medical men, but we never realized their significance. Now Pasteur—and he calls them germs—has seen what they are and what they do."

Agnes stared into his face. Cautiously she said, "You were speaking of this Pasteur and his experiments with wine and milk. What does that have to do with living human tissue?"

"Pasteur has proved that these germs live in dust in the air. I am sure, even without seeing these germs myself, that they cause the fluid in sick, irritated tissues to begin the rot which we call gangrene!"

Lister's trained mind had leaped instantly from Pasteur's discovery of what germs could do in milk and alcohol to what germs could do to the fluid of the body. But now he had to prove it to himself and others.

The study in his home began to resemble a chemist's laboratory. He first had to repeat Pasteur's experiments to prove there were such things as germs and to see what they did. He saw them in milk and in sugar-water mixtures. But in samples of discharges from infected wounds he saw nothing.

Agnes expected him to be disappointed. Instead, he was confident and undisturbed. "They *have* to be there, Aggie," he

---

putrefaction—*decay*
Leeuwenhoek (lā′vən·ho͝ok)

discharge—*liquid given off by an infected wound*

said. "The germ theory is true. Even if I can't see the germs with my own eyes, I can see the result and I am sure that our hospital murderers are these germs. I am sure that it is going to be possible to protect the wound so the germs cannot enter, and possible to kill those which do reach the blood and tissue."

Lister strode up and down the study. His usually calm face was alight with the hope of a miracle.

Agnes felt a little giddy. It had all happened so fast! Before her eyes her husband was becoming a new person. From the painstaking researcher he had stepped across an invisible line and was now existing in his own never-before-discovered country, which no other eyes but his had seen.

Unknown to Lister, there were other medical scientists who had read Pasteur's germ theory and saw these germs as disease breeders. They were busy isolating a single germ for a single disease. Only Lister saw germs from a surgical viewpoint. He had two gigantic problems to solve: to prove that germs cause gangrene and infection and to prevent these germs from getting into an open cut resulting from an accident, or into a surgical incision.

Early one morning he went to his study. Using the most powerful lens he owned, he looked at a single drop of diseased blood under the microscope, and he saw them! Incredibly tiny, so innocent in appearance—but these were germs and he knew them to be the killers he was looking for. They were alive. They were multiplying.

He went downstairs to breakfast. "My students will have a surprise this morning," he said to Agnes. "Today they are going to meet a germ."

The entire class was waiting for him at eight o'clock. When he came in, they were astonished to see that he carried in his hands four glass flasks instead of his usual pile of papers.

---

giddy—*dizzy*

flasks—*long-necked containers used in a laboratory*

"Today, gentlemen," he said, "we are going to conduct an experiment. This is the experiment of a Frenchman, Louis Pasteur."

He set the flasks on the desk. All four were wide at the bottom and tapered into thin necks.

"Observe, please, that the neck of one flask has been cut off short and is exposed to the air directly. The other three, as you are no doubt puzzled to see, have necks that curve up and then down in an abrupt, sharp angle. But they, too, are open to the air. None of these flasks are sealed."

Now he carefully filled all four flasks with a fluid. "This is a solution of sugar and water, with a little mineral substance added. It is sweet and pure." Then he heated all four flasks so that the liquid bubbled inside them. "I am heating the liquid to make absolutely certain that it is pure."

"Now"—turning off the flame under each one of them—"we will let the flasks cool. Each morning we will examine them and you will see whether Louis Pasteur is right or wrong." He stood directly in front of the class. "The theory is this: the liquid I used is of the type that ordinarily ferments easily if exposed to the air. Yet I can promise you now that only one of those flasks will have fermented liquid in it."

He saw the expression of disbelief on their faces and went on to explain: "Fermentation is not caused by the air itself. It is caused by germs. Remember that word—*germs.*"

Three days later Lister arrived to find the students gathered about the desk, exclaiming at what they saw. "The three with the bent necks are just the same as they were. But this one—it's cloudy and thick!"

The class was so excited Joseph had difficulty in getting everyone to sit down. "As I told you, the process of fermentation has started in the flask with the short neck, the one that is straight and open to the air. In this one the germs had free entry with nothing to stop them. But in the other three—"

"They were caught by the sharp curve of the necks!" A student completely forgot his classroom manners and shouted it out. Ordinarily, Joseph would have reproved him for shouting, but now he smiled at the young man's quickness. "I invite you to ask questions," he said to the class.

"Mr. Lister, are these germs beneficial to mankind?"

"Sometimes they are, sometimes not. They turn fresh milk sour. I have seen these same germs in the discharge of body tissue that has become infected."

There was total silence in the room. Where, before, their minds had been turned to his in understanding of what he was saying, now the class looked at each other, obviously puzzled. Joseph saw that the jump he could make from sour milk to decomposition in the body was not yet possible for them. A liquid in a flask was one thing, but the body was quite something else.

---

decomposition—*decay*

"We will discuss this again some other day. Louis Pasteur found that there are three methods of defeating the purpose of these germs. Two we have seen: heat and filtration. But there is still a third method. In our field of work we call it *antiseptics*."

Hector Cameron, Lister's assistant, had sat in on the lecture. The two men walked to the carriage that would take them to the hospital. Cameron was silent for a long time before he blurted out. "Chief, are you certain there are such things as germs? They sound like a fairy story: little things in the air which we can't see but which are alive and behave just like other living things."

Again Joseph patiently explained the microscopic studies he had made. He went on, "I think the skin on our bodies is like the glass of those bottles—a delicate covering but sufficient to keep out germs. If the skin, like those glasses, has a break or an opening, the germs get in. What we need, Hector, is a solution—an antiseptic that will prevent germs from reaching the body—and will kill any that do."

"What would it be?"

"I don't know. I'll have to find it."

Once again Dr. Lister, with the help of his wife, pored over documents and medical journals. Antiseptics were not new. They had been used in ancient Egypt to embalm the dead. Chloride of lime was frequently used to purify a room, but the purpose for which Lister now intended antiseptics was new.

One night he read a report from the city of Carlisle. The health and sanitation authorities there had found that carbolic acid had effectively quenched all the terrible odors that had been polluting the air from their garbage dump.

"The odor." That was what caught Lister's eye. If carbolic acid could stop the stench of pollution, it meant that it had killed the source of the odor. It had killed the germs causing decomposition.

The carbolic acid he bought the next day was heavy and dark, and it had its own powerful smell, but at least it smelled clean.

"Everything I've read about carbolic," he said to Agnes, "makes it seem a powerful but safe antiseptic. I'm going to try it."

"Try it? On a patient?" She watched his face and felt that he was almost a stranger. It was as if he were living in a strange country where only he knew the way.

"Yes. There is no danger. But I shall try it only in cases of compound fracture, where the skin has been broken and the wound is the particularly ugly kind that usually leads to gangrene. Most of those cases have little chance of survival anyhow."

In March 1865, Lister found his first opportunity to test his theory. A man had been brought in with a terrible wound on the right leg. He had not come to the hospital when he was first hurt but had stayed at home. Now the spark of life in him was almost gone.

Lister carefully soaked the wound with cloths saturated with carbolic acid. Then he left another wet cloth around the leg. If he was right, this would prevent the germs from getting into the wound. Joseph confidently expected that the carbolic would arrest the progress of gangrene and give the body a chance to begin its healing.

But the next morning the patient was dead. Lister received the news calmly. "Poor fellow," he said. "He hadn't a chance. Too far gone when they brought him here. Now we've learned what we should have known before. When the cells have lost vitality, but not too much, they can recover. I should not have expected a miracle. We must wait for another patient, one whose body has a fighting chance."

Five months later Lister was able to test his theory again. On an August morning he arrived at the hospital and was greeted with important news.

---

arrest—*stop*

230

"We have a young lad only eleven years old in the ward today," his assistant said. "A bad case. A cart ran over his left leg and broke both bones. There's a wound through the skin an inch and half long. Will you look at the boy now?"

"At once, please."

In the ward Lister bent over the bed and smiled at the boy. "What is your name?"

"Jimmy Greenlees," the boy whispered.

"Well, Jimmy, you're a brave boy not to cry after such an accident."

Lister examined the wound. Then it was dressed with cloths soaked in carbolic. The strong smell of the acid made Jimmy's eyes water. "But I'm not crying," he explained.

Lister patted the boy's arm. To his assistant he said, "Now I want the lad carried to the operating table—carefully. Under no circumstances is the cloth to be disturbed or touched by anyone."

When the boy was under the anesthetic, Lister set the bones with infinite care and put them into splints. Then the boy was carried back to his bed, with the carbolic bandage in place.

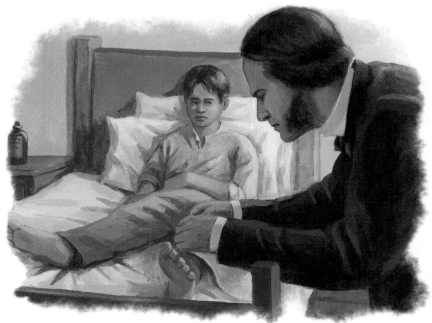

"You think that carbolic stuff will cure him, Mr. Lister?" one of his dressers asked. He and the nurses were wide-eyed with curiosity at what was going on.

"Not cure. No. An antiseptic is not a cure. The body will heal itself if we give it a chance to do so, and that's what the carbolic is for. It should kill the germs and prevent them from reaching the wound."

One of the nurses ran out of the room, giggling. By night-fall it was all over the hospital that Joseph Lister had been taken in by a crazy germ idea which some Frenchman had cooked up and that Joseph Lister thought he could kill these nonexistent beasts with carbolic acid. Some doctors laughed; others shook their heads in disapproval.

Four times that day Lister visited the boy and carefully wet the cloth with more carbolic acid, but he did not remove it or change it or lift it from the skin. By the fourth visit, the young patient managed a smile.

The second and third days went well. On the morning of the fourth day Lister went to the ward with greater urgency than he had before. It was usually on the fourth day that symptoms of gangrene began to show.

He was greeted by a most unhappy assistant. "I hate to tell you this, Chief, but Jimmy's complaining of a new pain in his leg."

For a moment Lister could not make his feet move to take him to the bedside. Another failure! What could have gone wrong?

Sadly he went to Jimmy's bed. "Is it very bad, son?" he asked. Sadly he put his hand to the boy's forehead. It was cool. No fever.

The surgeon pulled down the bed covers and looked at the leg. Carefully he took off the splints and then peeled off the bandage. Both he and his assistant examined the wound with growing excitement. There was no swelling. No discharge.

"This is what is causing the mischief." Lister pointed to a small section of skin that had been burned slightly by the carbolic acid.

A soothing ointment was put on the burn. "Am I going to get well, Mr. Lister?" Jimmy asked. When he had been picked up in the street after the accident, his mother had screamed in fear that his leg would have to be cut off.

The surgeon hesitated a moment. Four days were not much of a test. Then he said confidently, "You will be well, my lad."

The days went by.

"Aggie," he said to his wife one evening, "I can say definitely that the experiment has been a success. The boy is getting well. The leg is saved. Not only that, he has been saved all the torture of even those who do recover—he's had none of the discharge or the swelling or fever. He will walk again as well as he ever did."

"The other surgeons in the hospital must be very curious and excited about what you are doing!" said Agnes.

"If they are, I have seen no evidence of it." He leaned his head back against the pillow of his chair. The tension that had been in his face was gone.

In a week he lifted the bandage again. The injured leg looked very healthy. In a very short time the boy was fully recovered.

What a proud day for both surgeon and patient when Jimmy walked slowly but firmly, with no help, down the hospital steps into the arms of his joyful mother.

Character Theme—Determination & Initiative

Time to Think

1. Who discovered the reason for fermentation?   What country was he from?
2. Explain why the liquid in only one flask in the experiment fermented.
3. What three ways did Pasteur find to defeat germs and stop them from spoiling food and spreading disease?
4. Do antiseptics heal? Why didn't the carbolic acid help the man with the terrible wound on his leg?
5. How did many people react when they heard about Dr. Lister's theories? Was he discouraged?
6. People who accomplish great things often share the same characteristics that Dr. Lister had. Describe these characteristics.

The Viceroy and the Indian

E. A. Davis

There was once a great viceroy who ruled in Mexico. He was called Count Revillagigedo. He had several other names and titles, too, but this one will be enough to remember. He was a good ruler, because he was not satisfied to listen to what his servants or officers told him but found out for himself what needed to be done for the country and the people. After he came to be viceroy, the streets of the city were cleaned, dark corners and alleys were better lighted at night, and the mudholes were filled up. More than that, he made a rule that he would see anyone, rich or poor, who came to him for justice or for help. So the people trusted him.

One morning a poorly dressed Indian came to Count Revillagigedo's door and stood there silently and respectfully. For a while, he said nothing. At last he asked rather timidly if the viceroy was at home.

viceroy—*a person ruling in place of the king*
Revillagigedo (rä·vē′yä·hē·hā′dō)

"Where else would he be at this hour?" asked the guard, who didn't feel it necessary to show respect to a poor Indian.

So the Indian waited a while longer. Then another guard asked him what he wanted, and this time he asked to see the viceroy. The guard was not very polite about showing him in, but since the viceroy had ordered that anyone who wished it was to see him, he led the man to the viceroy's apartment. As the Indian stood there quietly, the viceroy came in, greeted him pleasantly and asked, "How can I be of service to you, señor?"

At this, the Indian began to tell his story, talking slowly.

"Two nights ago, Your Excellency, I was walking through a *calle* (street) when I noticed a small bag lying almost in my path. I picked it up and carried it to my *caseta* (little house), where I opened it and found that it contained gold coins. It was full of them. Since I had seen no one around when I found the bag, I did not know who the owner might be, and I decided to keep it until morning. So I hid it in a corner of my house and covered it with a straw mat. Then I went to sleep.

"Next morning the crier came through my street and called out that a wealthy Spanish Don (nobleman) had lost a bag of gold coins and that he had offered a reward to the one who would return the bag to him. Señor, I thought long and hard. I am a poor man. I wish to marry the girl I have chosen for my wife, and I wish to have a better house. These golden coins would be a fortune to me. But they are not mine, and when I thought of it, I knew I could not be happy keeping them. So I dressed myself carefully and went to the Don's fine house, hoping he would give me one coin for reward. The servants let me in and took me to him. He was sitting there, drinking with some other men, his friends. I went straight to him and handed him the bag and told him that I had found it the night before.

---

señor—*Spanish title for a man*
crier—*a person who shouts out public announcements*

236

"Then, señor, he took the bag quickly, opened it and began to count the coins. That wasn't all he did. I saw him with my own eyes. As he counted the coins, he took out two and slipped them into the pocket of his coat. When he had finished counting, he said to me, 'There were twenty-eight coins in this bag, and now there are only twenty-six. You have stolen the other two. Since you are a thief, why should I give you a reward? Get out now, or I'll call the police and have you sent to the *calabozo* (jail), where you belong.' And then, señor, they put me out."

He was silent a moment, and then he drew himself up straight and said, "Your Excellency, I did not steal those coins. I saw him take the coins and put them in his pocket."

The viceroy had looked steadily at the Indian while he was telling his story. Now he nodded and then stood up quickly and called a servant.

"Go to the house of this noble Don and tell him the viceroy wishes him to come at once and bring with him the bag of golden coins which he lost on the street day before yesterday."

In a few minutes the Don appeared, for it was well known that the viceroy did not like to be kept waiting. He bowed respectfully. The first words of the viceroy were these: "I hear you lost a bag which held gold coins and that this man returned it to you. Will you tell me just what occurred when he brought you the bag?"

The viceroy looked keenly at the rich man. The Don moved uneasily in his chair. His eyes shifted away from the viceroy's and he looked down at the floor. In his own mind, now, the viceroy was convinced of the truth, but he let the Don talk.

"Your most gracious Excellency," he began, "two days ago I lost this bag of gold coins. Yesterday morning this Indian brought it to me, with the hope, I suppose, that he would gain the reward I had offered." Here he hesitated, and then said, speaking rapidly, "But, Your Excellency, he had stolen part of the

money, so naturally I drove him from my house. He is a thief. He should be punished."

The great viceroy looked hard at the rich man; then he looked at the Indian, who was standing there very straight, not saying a word. After a full moment of silence, the viceroy looked back at the Don and said, "My dear sir, I much appreciate your telling me exactly what happened, but it is evident there is some mistake. How many coins did you say were in the bag you lost?"

"Twenty-eight, Your Excellency."

"And how many are in this bag now?"

"Only twenty-six, Your Excellency."

"Are you sure? Count them out so that we may be certain there is no mistake." The Don counted the coins slowly. There were only twenty-six.

"Thank you, sir, very much. The case is clear to me now. We have all been mistaken. This Indian is not the thief, for, if he were, he would never have brought you the bag. It is therefore quite evident that this is not your bag at all. It must belong to someone else. I am sorry that you have lost your money, and of course I hope it will be found. And now, sir, our interview is at an end. I bid you good day." And with that he led the much disappointed Don to the door and out of the room, without even giving him a chance for a backward look at the bag of coins lying on the table.

In a moment he returned, picked up the bag, and put it into the surprised Indian's hands.

"My friend," he said, "since you are an honest man, and since we cannot find the owner of this bag, it is clear that it should belong to you. Take these coins, for they are yours." And he laid his hand on the happy Indian's shoulder and showed him the door.

Character Theme—Honesty &
Justice

Time to Think

1. From what country does this story come?
2. What character qualities of the Indian show that, though he was poor, he was a great man?
3. Was the viceroy a good leader? Why?
4. Why is the ending to this story so satisfying?

I'm Not Running on a Sunday

Sally Magnusson

"I'm not running," he said, and nothing would budge him. He didn't make a fuss, but he was absolutely firm about it. The Sabbath was God's day, and he would not run. Not even in the Olympic Games.

The British athletics authorities were horrified. It was early in 1924, only a few months before the Eighth Olympics in Paris, and Eric Liddell was Britain's main hope for the 100 meters. He was their golden boy. And now he was saying he would not run in the qualifying heats of the 100 meters because they were being held on a Sunday. It was tantamount to throwing away a gold medal for Scotland, and for Britain.

Eric made his decision known as soon as the timetables for the Olympics were announced. "It was all very quiet," says his fellow student athlete, Professor Neil Campbell. "Liddell was the last person to make a song and dance about that sort of thing. He just said, 'I'm not running on a Sunday'—and that was that. And he would have been very upset if anything much had been made of it at the time. We thought it was completely in charac-

---

qualifying heats—*preliminary races to determine finalists*
tantamount—*equal*

ter, and a lot of the athletes were quietly impressed by it. They felt that here was a man who was prepared to stand for what he thought was right, without interfering with anyone else, and without being dogmatic or anything like that. Quietly, he just said, 'I'm not running on a Sunday.' "

Reverence for the Sabbath was as natural to Eric Liddell as breathing, and infinitely more precious than a gold medal. It probably didn't occur to him to try to rationalize it. Or did he have doubts? Did he try to persuade himself that he would be honoring God just as much by winning a race for Him as by having a Sabbath rest? Did he perhaps wonder if it would not be a finer thing to sacrifice his principles just this once for the sake of a gold for Scotland? But if these thoughts ever occurred to Eric Liddell, he did not voice them, or let them stay very long. Nor did he let press criticism or public jibes about 'national honour' change his mind, even though he was hurt by the comments and deeply unhappy about denying Scotland a rare and precious chance of excelling in the Blue Riband event of the Olympics.

"He was called a traitor to his country, and I think he felt it quite keenly," said his wife Florence, to whom he told the story many years later. But he had the support of many athletes, one of whom was so impressed by Eric's stand that he actually followed his example at another race meeting some time after the Olympics. The man was Tom Riddell, eight times the Scottish champion miler between 1925 and 1935. He used to run in medley relay races with Eric, with Riddell on the half-mile leg and Liddell on the quarter-mile. He describes Eric as "a terrific influence on all of us athletes at the time"—so much so that when Tom Riddell was chosen to run in a race-meeting in Italy, and learned that the race was to be run on a Sunday morning, he withdrew. "That was because of Eric's example," he says.

---

dogmatic—*characterized by arrogant stubbornness*

rationalize—*justify by selfish reasoning*
jibes—*mocking remarks*

"Without the slightest doubt, Eric Liddell was the greatest athlete Scotland has ever produced—by his influence, his example, and his capabilities."

Liddell was now out of the Olympic 100 meters sprint. The problem was what on earth to do with him. In the end he was asked to train instead for the 400 meters in Paris. And that was how Eric Liddell discovered that he was a natural quarter-miler.

"Eric always said that the great thing for him," his wife Florence recalls, "was that when he stood by his principles and refused to run in the 100 meters, he found that the 400 meters was really his race. He said he would never have known that otherwise. He would never have dreamed of trying the 400 at the Olympics."

Eric Liddell trained hard in the few months left to him before the big race. His blood was up now, but he had a long way to go. At the AAA Championships held within a few weeks of the Olympics, he had fended off British, Canadian, and American opposition to run in the respectable time of 49.6 seconds. But his chances of beating the cluster of Olympic entrants, all of whom were credited with times around 48 seconds, looked extremely remote.

The Paris Games ushered in a new era in the Olympic movement. They opened on Saturday, July 5, 1924, to a crowd of about 60,000. There were forty-four nations competing this time, fifteen more than at Antwerp, and more than 3,000 participants, some 500 more than last time.

But the thing that everyone would remember the 1924 Olympics for was the searing heat. Never before had the games been staged in the sort of heat in which the Colombes Stadium sweltered that month of July. A "cauldron," some called the stadium—others preferred "furnace"; and one of the refreshment stalls was dubbed *La Bonne Frite* ("The Good Fry"). On some

---

fended off—*defeated*
sweltered—*suffered from extreme heat*

cauldron—*a large pot used for boiling*

days the temperature was as high as 113°F. Runners in the 10,000 meters cross-country race were dropping like flies, and only twenty-three of the thirty-eight starters finished the course.

The 2nd Queen's Own Cameron Highlanders were stationed in Cologne at the time, and were sent to Paris as the official British musicians for the Olympics. Their first duty was to lead the march of the British athletes up the Champs-Elysées to lay a wreath at the tomb of the Unknown Warrior. HRH Edward, Prince of Wales, laid the wreath, and four pipers played that infinitely poignant lament "The Flowers of the Forest," which mourns the calamitous Scottish defeat at the Battle of Flodden in 1513.

Captain Philip Christison was in charge that day. In the front row of the party of British athletes he noticed his fellow Scot, Eric Liddell—someone he would see a good deal more of that week, because they had both found themselves staying at the same Hôtel du Louvre. Captain Christison had the task of getting Liddell and the other British athletes to the stadium in time for their events. Despite the innovation of huts near the stadium, many of the athletes were still scattered in hotels all over the city. The Americans complicated the process by carrying their competitive spirit to the streets, and monopolizing the taxis at higher fares than anyone else could offer. The harassed British captain had to resort to stopping private cars in the street and pleading with the drivers to get the athletes to the race in time. The Olympics were a lot of fun in those days.

Liddell and the captain met from time to time in the hotel lounge for a chat, and Eric confided to him that his decision not to run in the 100 meters still weighed heavily on his mind.

"I wonder if I'm doing the right thing?" he would say. But he always added a minute later, "No, I'm sure I'm right." The captain, now General Sir Philip Christison, says Eric was still under pressure from his teammates to run the 100 meters. There

---

Cologne (kō·lōn′)—*a German city on the Rhine River*

HRH—*His Royal Highness*
poignant (poin′yənt)—*touching the emotions*

243

was no acrimony in it, but Eric felt keenly that he was letting his country down. It was so rare for a Scot to reach this class in athletics and, yes, he felt it.

He was hardly allowed to forget that his behavior was considered to have been "less than cricket." Lord Cadogan, who was among the numerous British dignitaries at the Games, had given the team a little pep-talk at the start: "To play the game is the only thing in life that matters," he had said. Was he aware of Eric Liddell's eyes on him as he said it? Whether or not his words were an implicit rebuke to Liddell, *The Scotsman* heaped its own coals of fire when it reported them the next day. "There is not the least doubt," said the paper, "that the British team will play up and play the game, thus upholding the honor and repu-tation of Great Britain."

On the day when he should have been on the sprint track doing what Lord Cadogan considered the only thing in life that matters, Eric Liddell was preaching at a Scots church in another part of Paris.

On the following day, Monday, July 7, Liddell was back in the Stade Colombes to cheer Harold Abrahams on to victory in the semi-final and final of the 100 meters. Abrahams was the first European to win this, the most coveted of sprinting honors.

On Tuesday, July 8, Liddell cruised through the heats of the 200 meters. Abrahams and William Nichol of Great Britain were also through. On the same day, Douglas Lowe won the 800 meters for Britain in just half a second outside record time.

Wednesday, July 9, saw Liddell and Abrahams lined up together with four Americans for the final of the 200 meters. It was won by Jackson Scholz in a record 21.6 seconds, with Charles Paddock second. *The Scotsman* informed its readers the next day that Abrahams had been sixth and last; halfway through its description of just how Abrahams had gone about being last it

---

acrimony—*bitterness*
less than cricket—*a British phrase meaning inappropriate*

implicit—*understood, but not spoken*

244

casually offered the additional information that "Eric Liddell, the Scottish sprinter, scored points for Britain by running into third place." It notes that he failed to produce his strong finish, and adds: "He was well placed and had his spurt been forthcoming he would undoubtedly have won." The fact that Liddell had won a bronze medal for Britain at his first Olympic appearance, and that he was the first Scot ever to win an Olympic medal in the 200 meters, was not brought to the readers' attention.

On Thursday, July 10, Liddell cruised through his first-round heat of the 400 meters in the mediocre time of 50.2, well behind the winner. Later that day he won his quarter-final in a personal best of 49.0. Next day he won his semi-final in 48.2; Liddell was clearly coming into top form at exactly the right moment. His time, however, was slower than that of the American Horatio Fitch, who had just shattered the world and Olympic record in the other semi-final in 47.8, and of the Swiss runner Joseph Imbach, not to mention the gallant Guy Butler who had qualified for the final in a European and UK record of 48.0. There was little to suggest, that Friday afternoon, that Liddell would take world athletics by storm on the same evening.

On the morning of that momentous day, Friday, July 11, Eric had been handed a note. It read: "In the old book it says, 'He that honors me I will honor.' Wishing you the best of success always." It was signed by the athletics masseur who attended to Eric and the rest of the British team. The biblical reference he had in mind was 1 Samuel 2, verse 30: "Them that honor me, I will honor." He wrote it, as he revealed later, simply because he "liked Eric so much."

The Stade Colombes was baking hot when the six competitors gathered on the track for the 400 meters final. There were two Britons (Liddell and Butler), two Americans (Horatio Fitch and Conrad Taylor), a Swiss (Joseph Imbach), and a Canadian

---

mediocre—*average to less than average*
masseur (mă·sûr′)—*person whose work is giving massages*

(David Johnson). Liddell went round shaking hands with all his opponents before the start as usual, and his masseur says that he must have been saying good-bye to them because they wouldn't be seeing him again—he would be so far in front. That sounds like hindsight: Liddell had been drawn in the dreaded outside lane—the worst possible place for a relative novice at the event— where he would have to set the pace on his own without knowing how his opponents were faring.

Suddenly there was a blast of pipes and a swirl of kilts. It was the Cameron Highlanders: with a fellow Scot in the final of the 400 meters and a pipe-band only fifty yards away, the temptation had been irresistible. "Oh, we just wanted to give Liddell a lift," says General Sir Philip Christison. "The atmosphere was so light-hearted that I said 'Come on, let's strike up'—and there was nothing the French could do to stop us." They marched around the arena playing "The Campbells are Coming." (Liddell joked to a reporter from the London *Evening Standard* the next day that he suspected either the army general or the British team captain of a dark plot to terrify the opposition!)

At last the stirring strains of the pipes died away. The six finalists settled in their marks and tensed. The pistol cracked, and Eric Liddell in the outside lane was off like a greyhound. People still remember with awe the blistering pace he set in the first half of that incredible race. He flashed past the 200-meter mark at 22.2 seconds—only 0.6 of a second slower than Scholz's winning time in the 200 meters final two days earlier. He was now some three meters clear of his nearest rival, the bandaged Guy Butler, who was making a tremendous effort on the inside.

There was no possibility of Liddell keeping it up, the aficionados were thinking in the stands: *no one* could sprint the first 200 meters of a 400-meter race flat out, and stay the pace to the end. He was bound to "blow up" in the home straight, if

novice—*a beginner*
aficionados (ə·fĭsh′ē·ə·nä′dōz)—*spectators; fans*

not earlier. Besides, there was his ungainly energy-wasting style, arms flailing and knees pumping.

As the runners came off the bend into the straight (there was only one bend at the Stade Colombes, because the track was 500 meters, which meant the 400-meter track wasn't a full circuit), Fitch was beginning to make up ground. He had overtaken Guy Butler (who would win the bronze) and was now chasing hard after Liddell, who was only two meters ahead of him.

And then the incredible happened. At the moment when any other runner would have started to flag, however determined, Eric Liddell somehow summoned up hidden reserves of strength and stamina. Head back, chin forward, mouth open, knees jumping, arms waving, he put on a spurt and started to *increase* his lead over Fitch. At the tape he was all of five meters ahead, and had won the Olympic title in a world record time of 47.6.

---

ungainly—*awkward, clumsy*
flag—*get tired*

To anyone who knows anything about running, that sensational race was, and still is, almost unbelievable.

To give *The Scotsman* its due, its report on the inside pages was unrestrained:

> The Union Jack flew in proud majesty over the Colombes Stadium today for the only final down for decision, the 400 meters, which resulted in a great victory for Great Britain. The brilliant running of E. H. Liddell, the Edinburgh University sprinter, was responsible.
>
> There was a gasp of astonishment when Eric Liddell, one of the most popular athletes at Colombes, was seen to be a clear three yards ahead of the field at the half distance. Nearing the tape Fitch and Butler strained every nerve and muscle to overtake him, but could make absolutely no impression on the inspired Scot. With twenty yards to go, Fitch seemed to gain a fraction, but Liddell appeared to sense the American, and with his head back and chin thrust out in his usual style, he flashed past the tape to gain what was probably the greatest victory of the meeting. Certainly there has not been a more popular win. The crowd went into a frenzy of enthusiasm, which was renewed when the loud-speaker announced that once again the world's record had gone by the board.

The Edinburgh *Evening News* was even more ebullient:

> All around the banked area, people were on their feet cheering madly, and as if

---

Union Jack—*the flag of Great Britain*
ebullient (ĭ·bŏͅol′yənt)—*overflowing with enthusiasm*

by magic, hosts of Union Jacks appeared above the heads of the raving crowd as Liddell ripped through the tape and into the arms of the Britishers who were waiting for him. For a moment the cheering lasted, then from the loudspeaker came: "Hello, hello. Winner of the 400 meters: Liddell of Great Britain. The time 47 $\frac{3}{5}$ is a new world's record." Again the great roar of cheering went up, and there were long minutes before the announcer could convey that Fitch, of America, was second and that Butler, who ran second in this event to Rudd, the South African at Antwerp, was third and Johnson, of Canada, fourth. Thrill followed thrill, for the flags went up, a big Union Jack in the center, a little one to the left, and a little Stars and Stripes to the right, and again came that hush as all the spectators stood and the bands played. Then came crash upon crash of applause as Liddell walked across the grass and vanished down the stairs to the dressing rooms.

Liddell's time of 47.6 seconds was officially ratified as a world record for the 400 meters. It was not the fastest time in the world, however; the great American runner, Ted Meredith, had earlier recorded 47.4 for the 440 yards, which is more than two meters longer. But Meredith had nothing but praise for Liddell, after watching the race from the stands. He told a reporter that it was the most wonderful quarter-mile that had ever been run. Considering the conditions under which it was run, it was nothing short of marvelous, as Liddell had had to make his own pace from the crack of the pistol to the tape. "Liddell," said Meredith, "is the greatest quarter-miler ever seen."

---

ratified—*verified, confirmed*

Liddell did not stay around for long in the stadium after his race. He had an address to deliver on Sunday at a church service in the old Scots Kirk in Paris for all the Olympic competitors, and he slipped away quietly to prepare it. Behind him, pencils scribbled and wires buzzed and the race was relived on a thousand tongues. Already they were speculating: Would he have won the race he never entered—the 100 meters? It has been asked many times since, and it remains the great unknowable.

But fifty-six years and twelve Olympics later, somebody else, in a curious, fanciful sort of way, ran the 100 meters race for him. A Scotsman won the jewel of the sprint titles at last. And when Allan Wells was asked after the race if he had run it for Harold Abrahams, the British winner from 1924, Wells replied quietly: "No, this one was for Eric Liddell."

Character Theme—Honor & Sacrifice

Time to Think

1. What did Eric Liddell say that shocked his country?
2. Were his fellow athletes shocked?
3. What can we learn from Eric's reaction to criticism?
4. What unexpected blessing came as a result of Eric's standing for his convictions?
5. How did 1 Samuel 2:30 prove true in Eric's life?

WORK LOYALLY

Author Unknown

Just where you stand in the conflict,
    There is your place!
Just where you think you are useless,
    Hide not your face!
God placed you there for a purpose,
    Whate'er it be;
Think He has chosen you for it—
    Work loyally.

Gird on your armor! Be faithful
    At toil or rest,
Whiche'er it be, never doubting
    God's way is best.
Out in the fight, or on picket,
    Stand firm and true;
This is the work which your Master
    Gives you to do.

---

picket—*guard duty*

251

Chanticleer and Partlet

*Retold by J. Berg Esenwein
and Marietta Stockard*

Once there was a barnyard close to a wood, in a little valley. Here dwelt a cock, Chanticleer by name. His comb was redder than coral, his feathers were like burnished gold, and his voice was wonderful to hear. Long before dawn each morning his crowing sounded over the valley, and his seven wives listened in admiration.

One night as he sat on the perch by the side of Dame Partlet, his most loved mate, he began to make a curious noise in his throat.

"What is it, my dear?" said Dame Partlet. "You sound frightened."

"Oh!" said Chanticleer, "I had the most horrible dream. I thought that as I roamed down by the wood a beast like a dog sprang out and seized me. His color was red, his nose was small, and his eyes were like coals of fire. Ugh! It was fearful!"

"Tut, tut! Are you a coward to be frightened by a dream? You've been eating more than was good for you. I wish my husband to be wise and brave if he would keep my love!" Dame Partlet clucked, as she smoothed her feathers, and slowly closed her scarlet eyes. She felt disgusted at having her sleep disturbed.

"Of course you are right, my love, yet I have heard of many dreams which came true. I am sure I shall meet with some

---

Chanticleer (chăn′tĭ·klēr′)   burnished—*well polished*
cock—*rooster*

252

misfortune, but we will not talk of it now. I am quite happy to
be here by your side. You are very beautiful, my dear!"

Dame Partlet unclosed one eye slowly and made a pleased
sound, deep in her throat.

The next morning, Chanticleer flew down from the perch
and called his hens about him for their breakfast. He walked
about boldly, calling, "Chuck! chuck!" at each grain of corn
which he found. He felt very proud as they all looked at him so
admiringly. He strutted about in the sunlight, flapping his wings
to show off his feathers, and now and then throwing back his
head and crowing exultantly. His dream was forgotten; there was
no fear in his heart.

Now all this time, Reynard, the fox, was lying hidden in the
bushes on the edge of the wood bordering the barnyard. Chanticleer walked nearer and nearer his hiding place. Suddenly he
saw a butterfly in the grass, and as he stooped toward it, he spied
the fox.

"Cok! cok!" he cried in terror, and turned to flee.

"Dear friend, why do you go?" said Reynard in his gentlest
voice. "I only crept down here to hear you sing. Your voice is
like an angel's. Your father and mother once visited my house. I

should so love to see you there too. I wonder if you remember your father's singing? I can see him now as he stood on tiptoe, stretching out his long slender neck, sending out his glorious voice. He always flapped his wings and closed his eyes before he sang. Do you do it in the same way? Won't you sing just once and let me hear you? I am so anxious to know if you really sing better than your father."

Chanticleer was so pleased with this flattery that he flapped his wings, stood on tiptoe, shut his eyes and crowed as loudly as he could.

No sooner had he begun then Reynard sprang forward, caught him by the throat, threw him over his shoulder, and made off toward his den in the woods.

The hens made a loud outcry when they saw Chanticleer being carried off, so that the people in the cottage nearby heard and ran out after the fox. The dog heard and ran yelping after him. The cow ran, the calf ran, the pigs began to squeal and run too. The ducks and geese quacked in terror and flew up into the treetops. Never was there heard such an uproar. Reynard began to feel a bit frightened himself.

"How swiftly do you run!" said Chanticleer from his back. "If I were you I should have some sport out of those slow fellows who are trying to catch you. Call out to them and say, 'Why do you creep along like snails? Look! I am far ahead of you and shall soon be feasting on this cock in spite of all of you!' "

Reynard was pleased at this and opened his mouth to call to his pursuers; but as soon as he did so, the cock flew away from him and perched up in a tree safely out of reach.

The fox saw he had lost his prey and began his old tricks again. "I was only proving to you how important you are in the barnyard. See what a commotion we caused! I did not mean to frighten you. Come down now and we will go along together to my home. I have something very interesting to show you there."

"No, no," said Chanticleer. "You will not catch me again. A man who shuts his eyes when he ought to be looking deserves to lose his sight entirely."

By this time, Chanticleer's friends were drawing near, so Reynard turned to flee. "The man who talks when he should be silent deserves to lose what he has gained," he said as he sped away through the wood.

Character Theme—Humility

Time to Think

1. Why did Chanticleer enjoy flattery so much?
2. How did Reynard trick Chanticleer?
3. How did Chanticleer escape from Reynard's mouth?
4. What lesson does this story teach about flattery?

Hiawatha's Childhood

Henry Wadsworth Longfellow

MEET THE AUTHOR

Henry Wadsworth Longfellow (1807–1882), from New England, became the most popular American poet of the 19th century. Some of his best known works include "The Village Blacksmith," "The Children's Hour," and "Paul Revere's Ride."

> By the shores of Gitche Gumee,
> By the shining Big-Sea-Water,
> Stood the wigwam of Nokomis,
> Daughter of the Moon, Nokomis.
> Dark behind it rose the forest,
> Rose the black and gloomy pine-trees,
> Rose the firs with cones upon them;
> Bright before it beat the water,
> Beat the clear and sunny water,
> Beat the shining Big-Sea-Water.

Gitche Gumee (gĭch′ē·gōō′mē)
Big-Sea-Water—*Lake Superior*
Nokomis (nŭ·kō′mĭs)—*Hiawatha's grandmother*

There the wrinkled old Nokomis
Nursed the little Hiawatha,
Rocked him in his linden cradle,
Bedded soft in moss and rushes,
Safely bound with reindeer sinews;
Stilled his fretful wail by saying,
"Hush! the Naked Bear will hear thee!"
Lulled him into slumber, singing,
"Ewa-yea! my little owlet!
Who is this, that lights the wigwam?
With his great eyes lights the wigwam?
Ewa-yea! my little owlet!"

At the door on summer evenings
Sat the little Hiawatha;
Heard the whispering of the pine-trees,
Heard the lapping of the waters.
Sounds of music, words of wonder;
"Minne-wawa!" said the pine trees,
"Mudway-aushka!" said the water.

Saw the fire-fly, Wah-wah-taysee,
Flitting through the dusk of evening,

---

linden—*a variety of shade tree having heart-shaped leaves*
sinews—*tendons used as ropes*
ewa-yea (ē′wä·yā′)—*lullaby*

With the twinkle of its candle
Lighting up the brakes and bushes,
And he sang the song of children.
Sang the song Nokomis taught him:
"Wah-wah-taysee, little fire-fly,
Little, flitting, white-fire insect,
Little, dancing, white-fire creature,
Light me with your little candle,
Ere upon my bed I lay me,
Ere in sleep I close my eyelids!"

Saw the rainbow in the heaven,
In the eastern sky, the rainbow,
Whispered, "What is that, Nokomis?"
And the good Nokomis answered:
"'Tis the heaven of flowers you see there;
All the wild-flowers of the forest,
All the lilies of the prairie,
When on earth they fade and perish,
Blossom in that heaven above us."

When he heard the owls at midnight,
Hooting, laughing in the forest,
"What is that?" he cried in terror,
"What is that," he said, "Nokomis?"
And the good Nokomis answered:
"That is but the owl and owlet,
Talking in their native language,
Talking, scolding at each other."

Then the little Hiawatha
Learned of every bird its language,
Learned their names and all their secrets,
How they built their nests in Summer,
Where they hid themselves in Winter,
Talked with them whene'er he met them,
Called them "Hiawatha's Chickens."

---

brakes—*undergrowth; thickets*
ere—*before*

Of all beasts he learned the language,
Learned their names and all their secrets,
How the beavers built their lodges,
Where the squirrels hid their acorns,
How the reindeer ran so swiftly,
Why the rabbit was so timid,
Talked with them whene'er he met them,
Called them "Hiawatha's Brothers."

Time to Think

1. What surrounded Nokomis's wigwam?
2. What did Nokomis call the baby Hiawatha at night?
3. What sound did the lapping water seem to make?
4. What animals did Hiawatha learn about?
5. What would you like to teach Hiawatha if you could meet him?

The Merchant of Venice

Judy Springfield
(adapted from the play by William Shakespeare)

William Shakespeare lived hundreds of years ago in England. Many people who love plays and poetry consider him to be the world's greatest dramatist and poet. He wrote at least thirty-seven plays. You probably recognize the names Romeo and Juliet, Macbeth, and Hamlet. They are characters in three famous Shakespearean plays. The following play is a shortened version of another popular play. Someday soon you will want to read the original version in Shakespeare's own beautiful words.

In Venice there lived a merchant whose name was Antonio. This man was known far and wide for his kindness and generosity. In fact, there were people all over Venice to whom Antonio had loaned money when they were in great need of such help.

Antonio was such a generous businessman that he would loan money to those he trusted without expecting to receive any money above the amount they borrowed. In other words, he charged no interest.

There was a money-lender in that city whose name was Shylock. He was perhaps the only one in Venice who did not like Antonio. There were two reasons why Shylock disliked the merchant. First, he disliked him because Antonio made loans without charging any interest. Shylock also disliked him for a second reason. Although he was kind to everyone else, Antonio had made fun of Shylock because he was Jewish. Shylock was one of the few people in Venice who were Jewish in their beliefs; he was also Hebrew in nationality.

It was very wrong of Antonio to be unkind to Shylock because of his beliefs. He thought that Shylock should become a Christian, but he was not acting much like a Christian himself when he made fun of Shylock in public, saying things that embarrassed him.

Shylock, on his part, was guilty of the same sort of thing, for he would often make fun of those who considered themselves to be Christians. He had to be a little more careful what he said in public, though, because he was so far outnumbered. He realized that the number of Jews in Venice was comparatively small.

Remember that Antonio was kind to everyone, except, perhaps, to Shylock. It isn't surprising that Antonio had many friends. Of all these, Bassanio was probably his very best friend.

One day, Antonio appeared to be sad. His friends asked him if he was worried about his ships at sea. Antonio had invested a great deal of money in them, and he would lose much of his wealth if they should be lost on their voyage.

Antonio assured his friends that his ships were not the cause of his worry. One friend suggested that Antonio might be in love, but he insisted this was not true. Antonio said to them,

> In sooth, I know not why I am so sad:
> It wearies me, you say it wearies you;
> But how I caught it, found it, or came by it,
> I am to learn;
> And such a want-wit sadness makes of me,
> That I have much ado to know myself.

Antonio was waiting for his best friend Bassanio, who had asked to meet him and to discuss something. Maybe Antonio was sad because he suspected his friend wanted a loan. At this time, with most of his money tied up in his investments at sea, he would not be able to loan Bassanio anything.

If Antonio did suspect that Bassanio wanted a loan, he was right. Poor Antonio! Bassanio already owed him a lot of money,

---

want-wit—*a person lacking intelligence*   much ado—*much trouble or struggling* and now he wanted to borrow even more. Many people would have been angry if they had been Antonio that day. Antonio somehow knew, though, that his friend was not trying to cheat him. He believed that Bassanio would pay back the money. Although he did not have enough on hand to loan his friend, he agreed to borrow some money from Shylock and to turn this money over to Bassanio.

You may wonder why Bassanio could not just go to Shylock himself for the loan. The problem was that Shylock would not be likely to loan money to Bassanio. He would never trust a man who already owed so much money to Antonio. Where would a poor man like Bassanio get enough money to pay back such a loan? Antonio, on the other hand, would have plenty of money as soon as his ships came in. Shylock disliked him, but he would probably be glad to do business with Antonio and to make a profit on the loan.

Imagine how surprised Antonio was when Shylock agreed to loan the money without asking for any interest in return! Antonio thought that perhaps he and Shylock would even become friends. As a joke, Shylock had the agreement written up requiring the loan to be repaid by a certain time. The document actually specified that, if the money had not been repaid by a particular date, Shylock could cut off a pound of Antonio's flesh.

Bassanio was horrified. He did not trust the money-lender and was afraid that something would go wrong. What if Bassanio could not repay the money to Antonio in time? That would mean Antonio would lose a pound of flesh. What if he ended up having his hand cut off, or one of his feet, or worse?

"You shall not seal to such a bond for me," he said to Antonio, "I'll rather dwell in my necessity."

Shylock seemed surprised that Bassanio was taking the joke so seriously. He reminded them that a pound of Antonio's flesh would certainly be worth nothing to him.

If he should break his day, what should I gain
By the exaction of the forfeiture?
A pound of man's flesh taken from a man
Is not so estimable, profitable neither,
As flesh of muttons, beefs, or goats.
   I say,
To buy his favor, I extend this friendship:
If he will take it, so; if not, adieu; . . .

Antonio agreed to sign the document. He knew that he would be able to pay the loan on time because he expected his ships to come in long before it was due. As soon as he borrowed the money, he turned it over to Bassanio, who used it to make an important journey he had been planning. Antonio urged him to enjoy his trip, but Bassanio still worried about the odd nature of the document his friend had signed.

There was a certain young lady in a place some distance from Venice whose name was Portia. Not only was she lovely in appearance, she was known also for her wisdom and kindness. In addition, she was extremely wealthy, but her mother and father were both dead. Portia lived in a luxurious mansion with her faithful maid, Nerissa, and a few other servants.

---

exaction of the forfeiture—*completion of the sacrifice*

With all her loveliness, kindness, wisdom, and wealth, it was only natural that many young men should seek Portia's hand in marriage. How would she know which of them was sincere? Surely there would be some among them who would be selfish, greedy, and deceitful. How would she know which of them was only interested in her wealth?

Before his death, Portia's wise father had thought about these questions. Perhaps he had realized that he was soon to die, and so he had left instructions in his will for his daughter. His plans were unique, as you shall see.

Anyone who came to ask Portia to marry him would have to agree to submit to a test. Before he was allowed to even take the test, he must promise never to tell anyone anything about it. He would have to promise, also, never to marry anyone if he should fail the test. A young man would surely think twice about making such promises!

Wealthy and important suitors came from far and near to seek Portia's hand in marriage. Many refused, however, to take the test because of the promises involved. A few even dared to take the test, but so far none of them had passed it.

The test itself was very strange. Three metal boxes were presented to the guest; he was asked to choose one of the three. If he chose the right one, the one containing a picture of Portia, he would be permitted to marry her.

One of the chests was made of gold; one was silver, and one was lead. Naturally, most people would choose the gold or silver. Any young man who chose the silver box would find a silly-looking picture which looked nothing like Portia, along with a note which read, "Who chooses me shall have as much as he deserves." Anyone choosing the gold chest would find a human skull with a message reading, "All that glitters is not gold. . . ." The box made of lead was not very shiny or pretty, but it was the one containing Portia's picture! So far, not one of her visitors had ever chosen the leaden box.

Portia's maid would ask her from time to time what she thought of this or that visitor, and Portia always replied that she was glad when one of them failed the test or refused to take it. So far, she had not met any man whom she loved. Once, however, she had met a man who seemed very nice. Perhaps, if she got to know him . . . who could tell? Yes, he did seem more interesting than any of the others. His name was Bassanio, and he lived far away, in Venice. Portia wasn't sure, but she thought she would like it if he should ever happen to come visit her.

Back in Venice, Shylock had some terrible news. His daughter, Jessica, had run away and taken some of his riches with her. Perhaps Shylock deserved for this to happen. Perhaps he had treated her cruelly, but the fact was that it made him very unhappy to lose his daughter. When a rumor reached Venice that Jessica had traded her father's expensive ring for a pet monkey, he was enraged.

How could Jessica be so thoughtless? His dear wife, now dead, had given him that ring before they were married. More news reached him that Jessica had married Lorenzo, a friend of Antonio's.

Shylock suspected that Antonio had encouraged Jessica to run away. It was true that some of his friends were involved in this, but Antonio had been occupied with his own misfortunes at the time.

Shylock, you see, was not the only one who received bad news that day. Antonio was notified that his ships had all been lost at sea, destroyed forever. There would be no way, now, that he could pay his debt to Shylock unless Bassanio returned from his journey immediately with enough money to cover it. In those days, with no regular system of mail, there was a slim chance that Bassanio could be notified in time. Antonio had urged his friend to take his time and not to rush home. He had been counting on his ships coming in laden with wealth from trading in foreign lands. Poor Antonio! His only hope was that

Shylock would show mercy. After all, the horrible penalty in
the document had been only a joke, hadn't it? Perhaps Shylock
would be willing to wait until Bassanio returned to Venice.

While Shylock and Antonio were grieving over their sepa-
rate misfortunes, Bassanio was visiting the beautiful mansion of
Belmont, where Portia lived. As Portia talked with Bassanio, she
grew to like him very much. In fact, she was beginning to think
that she was in love with him. She tried hard not to care too
much about him. What if he chose the wrong box? It seemed
as if all the others had been interested in the glory of winning
the contest and the wealth that they would gain. Bassanio, poor
though he was, really loved Portia. If he hoped to gain wealth, it
was only because of the money he owed to his friend, Antonio.
As for himself, all he wanted was to marry Portia and to do his
best to make her life happy.

Portia would not tell Bassanio which box to choose. She
had promised that she would follow her beloved father's instructions. Still, she hoped more and more that Bassanio would
choose the right box.

Bassanio looked carefully at each box. He noticed that
the leaden one had these words inscribed upon
it: "Who chooseth me must
give and hazard all he hath."

This message did not sound encouraging to most people, but Bassanio was attracted to it. He must have known that true love involved giving oneself for the sake of someone else. He chose the leaden casket and found Portia's picture inside!

Portia gladly admitted now that she loved Bassanio. Nerissa, her faithful maid, asked Portia if she would allow her to marry Bassanio's friend, Gratiano. This Gratiano had come to Belmont with Bassanio and had asked Nerissa to marry him. How happy Portia was for Nerissa, who had been more of a friend to her than a servant.

On the very day of their weddings, news arrived from Venice that every one of Antonio's ships had been destroyed. Since the date on the document was already passed, Shylock was demanding Antonio's payment in flesh! Bassanio, who had told Portia how poor he was when he first met her, now explained that he was worse than poor; that is, he owed money to Antonio. When Portia found out about Antonio's plight, she assured Bassanio that all her wealth was now his also. She urged him to take some money and travel quickly to Venice to try to save Antonio.

Bassanio and Gratiano left for Venice on their wedding day. After all, Antonio deserved their help; if it had not been for him, the two of them could not have traveled to Belmont in the first place. They could not have been happy until they knew Antonio was safe.

Portia, as you know, was not only beautiful and kind; she was very wise as well. She realized that money alone might not be enough to save Antonio. The debt to Shylock was already past due. This meant that Shylock had a legal right to claim the pound of flesh. If he hated Antonio enough, he might prefer to refuse any money Bassanio would offer.

Portia had an older cousin named Dr. Bellario. This man was a famous lawyer. Portia sent a servant to ask him for some legal advice and some articles of clothing. Soon Portia had disguised herself as a young lawyer. Nerissa disguised herself as the lawyer's clerk.

Portia and Nerissa rushed to the courtroom in Venice. Portia gave the duke a letter from her cousin, the famous lawyer. According to this letter, Portia was a young lawyer named Balthazar who had recently finished law school. The letter advised the court to let the young lawyer represent Antonio.

The duke thought that this Balthazar appeared to be a mere boy, hardly old enough to represent a client in court. Dr. Bellario said in the letter, however, that young Balthazar was very intelligent, practically a genius. The duke decided to take the old lawyer's advice and to allow Balthazar (Portia) to represent Antonio.

Poor Antonio had decided that he had no hope. As for Shylock, he was sitting in the courtroom, whetting his knife, so determined was he to take the pound of flesh. Naturally, he wanted to take it directly from Antonio's heart.

It could be that Shylock had really meant at first for the agreement to be a joke. Maybe he actually loaned the money to improve his relations with Antonio. If he did offer it with good intentions, the loss of his daughter and the portion of wealth she took from him had made him too bitter to be kind now.

Portia began by asking Shylock to show mercy. We know that mercy cannot be forced from a person by the law, since mercy is kindness directed to one who does not necessarily deserve it. Legally, it seemed that Antonio owed the pound of flesh, but Shylock could have acted nobly by forgiving the debt. Portia pointed out that mercy is one of the most wonderful qualities anyone can have. Even for a mighty king, mercy is perfectly in order. In fact, this quality of mercy is more important for a king than his royal crown. Portia told Shylock,

> The quality of mercy is not strained,
> It droppeth as the gentle rain from Heaven

---

whetting—*sharpening*

Upon the place beneath: it is twice blest;
It blesseth him that gives and him that takes:
'Tis mightiest in the mightiest: it becomes
The throned monarch better than his crown; . . .
It is enthroned in the hearts of kings,
It is an attribute of God himself;
And earthly power doth then show likest God's
When mercy seasons justice.

Not even this moving appeal for mercy could soften Shylock's heart. He would have his pound of flesh, and he would not even provide a doctor to attend the procedure. He was not willing to wait for Antonio's friends to get one, either. Bassanio tried to pay the debt and more in money, but Shylock was no longer interested in the money.

Finally, Portia had to admit,

A pound of that same merchant's flesh is thine:
The court awards it, and the law doth give it.

Shylock was delighted, but then the clever young "lawyer" added,

Tarry a little; there is something else.
This bond doth give thee here no jot of blood;
The words expressly are, 'a pound of flesh': . . .

She had found a loophole in the document at last! She went on to say that, if Shylock cut off a fraction more or less than a pound, or if he shed a drop of Antonio's blood, the whole procedure would be illegal. It may be that, with her cousin's advice in mind, Portia had this trick up her sleeve all along.

Bassanio was eager to be sure his friend was safe. He offered again to pay the money, but Portia reminded the court that this would be illegal now since Shylock had already openly refused the money.

By this time, Shylock saw that he was outwitted. He turned to leave the courtroom, but before he could leave, Portia

loophole—*a way of escape*

reminded the court of the penalty for plotting against the life of a Venetian citizen. After all, Shylock had plotted against Antonio's life! The penalty was that half of Shylock's riches could be confiscated by the government of Venice. The other half would go to Antonio. If the duke of Venice saw fit, Shylock could even be hanged as a murderer!

It must have been that Portia's eloquent words about mercy were still in the mind of the duke, for he immediately dropped the death penalty from Shylock's sentence. Antonio also showed mercy by dropping all charges if Shylock would do certain things; for one thing, Shylock must will all his wealth to Jessica and Lorenzo to be received by them after his death.

Bassanio and Gratiano must have been eager to return to Belmont and to tell their new brides, Portia and Nerissa, all about their exciting courtroom experiences. They would have a fine time telling them how the boy lawyer had won the case for Antonio! Best of all, they were planning to bring Antonio with them to meet their wives.

Little did they know that Portia and Nerissa had been right there in the courtroom! Who would have guessed that the young lawyer, Balthazar, was really Portia, who had probably never seen a law school in her life? Who would have thought that the lawyer's clerk was the maid, Nerissa, who had married Gratiano?

After the court was dismissed, the duke reminded Antonio to be sure the brilliant young lawyer was well paid for his excellent performance. Since Bassanio owed Antonio money anyway, he offered to take care of this matter.

Young Balthazar, however, would not take any money. He preferred to have some small souvenirs of this exciting day. From Antonio, he asked for a pair of his gloves. From Bassanio, he asked for the ring he was wearing.

Poor Bassanio did not want to give up the ring. His wife, Portia, had given it to him. Yet, he was ashamed to refuse such

a little thing when Balthazar had done so much. If only he had known that the young lawyer was really Portia!

When Portia told Nerissa of her mischief, Nerissa thought this was hilarious. She made up her mind to ask her husband Gratiano for his ring, too. After all, didn't the lawyer's clerk also deserve some payment?

The two young women left Venice quickly and arrived at Belmont before their husbands. Jessica and Lorenzo met them at the door; they had been looking after their house for them while they were away. They were happy to hear about the outcome of the trial.

When Bassanio and Gratiano finally came, they had their friend Antonio with them. What fun Portia and Nerissa had teasing their husbands about the rings! They both pretended to be quite hurt and unable to understand how their rings could have been given away.

Finally, Portia handed Bassanio "another" ring and asked him to keep up with it better than the first. Bassanio stared at it. Could it be? This was the very same ring he had given away!

Portia laughingly showed her husband a letter from her cousin explaining that she herself had been the so-called lawyer, Balthazar, and that Nerissa had been her clerk. She also had a letter for Antonio. It contained some very welcome news: three of his ships had come into port after all, laden with more riches than he could have hoped for!

Character Theme—Justice & Compassion

Time to Think

1. Where does this story take place?
2. What business was Shylock in?
3. What was strange about the deal that Shylock made with Antonio?
4. How was Bassanio different from Portia's other suitors?
5. Explain the "loophole" that Portia discovered in Shylock's contract.
6. In this story, Shakespeare tells us something about hatred and greed. What?

The Pied Piper of Hamelin

Robert Browning

I

Hamelin Town's in Brunswick
By famous Hanover city;
   The river Weser, deep and wide,
   Washes its wall on the southern side;
   A pleasanter spot you never spied;
But, when begins my ditty,
   Almost five hundred years ago,
   To see the townsfolk suffer so
      From vermin was a pity.

II

Rats!
They fought the dogs, and killed the cats,
   And bit the babies in the cradles,
And ate the cheeses out of the vats,
   And licked the soup from the cook's own ladles,
Split open the kegs of salted sprats,
Made nests inside men's Sunday hats,
And even spoiled the women's chats,
   By drowning their speaking
   With shrieking and squeaking
In fifty different sharps and flats.

III

At last the people in a body
To the Town Hall came flocking:
"'Tis clear," cried they, "our Mayor's a noddy;

---

pied—*having splotches of color*
Brunswick—*a region of northern Germany*
Weser (vā′zər)—*river in western Germany*
   that flows to the North Sea
vermin—*insects or rodents that are destructive*
sprats—*small ocean fish*
noddy—*a foolish person*

And as for our Corporation—shocking
To think that we buy gowns lined with ermine
For dolts that can't or won't determine
What's best to rid us of our vermin!
You hope, because you're old and obese,
To find in the furry civic robe ease?
Rouse up, sirs! Give your brain a racking
To find the remedy we're lacking,
Or, sure as fate, we'll send you packing!"
At this the Mayor and Corporation
Quaked with a mighty consternation.
An hour they sat in council,

IV

At length the Mayor broke silence:
"For a guilder I'd my ermine gown sell;
I wish I were a mile hence!
It's easy to bid one rack one's brain—
I'm sure my poor head aches again
I've scratched it so, and all in vain,
Oh for a trap, a trap, a trap!"
Just as he said this, what should hap
At the chamber door but a gentle tap?
"Bless us," cried the Mayor, "what's that?"
(With the Corporation as he sat,
Looking little though wondrous fat;
Nor brighter was his eye, nor moister,
Than a too-long-opened oyster,
Save when at noon his paunch grew mutinous
For a plate of turtle green and glutinous),
"Only a scraping of shoes on the mat?
Anything like the sound of a rat
Makes my heart go pit-a-pat!"

---

ermine—*a soft, white fur*
dolts—*unintelligent people*
consternation—*terror*
guilder—*a silver coin*
paunch—*a potbelly*
mutinous—*demanding to be acknowledged*
glutinous—*sticky*

V

"Come in!"—the Mayor cried, looking bigger:
And in did come the strangest figure.
His strange long coat from heel to head
Was half of yellow and half of red;
And he himself was tall and thin,
With sharp blue eyes, each like a pin,
And light loose hair, yet swarthy skin,
No tuft on cheek nor beard on chin,
But lips where smiles went out and in—
There was no guessing his kith and kin!
And nobody could enough admire
The tall man and his quaint attire.
Quoth one: "It's as my great grandsire,
Starting up at the Trump of Doom's tone,
Had walked this way from his painted tombstone."

VI

He advanced to the council-table:
And, "Please, your honours," said he, "I'm able,
By means of a secret charm, to draw
All creatures living beneath the sun,
That creep, or swim, or fly, or run,
After me so as you never saw!
And I chiefly use my charm
On creatures that do people harm,
The mole, and toad, and newt, and viper;
And people call me the Pied Piper."
(And here they noticed round his neck
A scarf of red and yellow stripe,
To match with his coat of the selfsame check;
And at the scarf's end hung a pipe;
And his fingers, they noticed, were ever straying
As if impatient to be playing
Upon this pipe, as low it dangled
Over his vesture so old-fangled.)

---

swarthy—*dark*
kith and kin—*friends and relatives*

"Yet," said he, "poor piper as I am,
In Tartary I freed the Cham,
Last June, from his huge swarms of gnats;
I eased in Asia the Nizam
Of monstrous brood of vampire bats:
And, as for what your brain bewilders,
If I can rid your town of rats
Will you give me a thousand guilders?"
"One? fifty thousand!"—was the exclamation
Of the astonished Mayor and Corporation.

VII

Into the street the Piper stept,
    Smiling first a little smile,
As if he knew what magic slept
    In his quiet pipe the while;
Then, like a musical adept,
To blow the pipe his lips he wrinkled,
And green and blue his sharp eyes twinkled
Like a candle-flame where salt is sprinkled;
And ere three shrill notes the pipe uttered,
You heard as if an army muttered;
And the muttering grew to a mighty grumbling;
And the grumbling grew to a mighty rumbling;
And out of the house the rats came tumbling.
Great rats, small rats, lean rats, brawny rats;
Brown rats, black rats, gray rats, tawny rats,
Grave old plodders, happy young friskers,
    Fathers, mothers, uncles, cousins,
Cocking tails and pricking whiskers,
    Families by tens and dozens,
Brothers, sisters, husbands, wives—
Followed the Piper for their lives.
From street to street he piped advancing,
And step by step they followed dancing,

Cham (chäm)—*a great ruler in India*
Nizam (nĭ·zäm′)—*formerly a title used for rulers in India*

Until they came to the river Weser
Wherein all plunged and perished
—Save one, who, stout as Julius Caesar,
Swam across and lived to carry
(As he the manuscript he cherished)
To Rat-land home his commentary,
Which was, "At the first shrill notes of the pipe,
I heard a sound as of scraping tripe,
And putting apples, wondrous ripe,
Into a cider press's gripe;
And a moving away of pickle-tub boards,
And a drawing the corks of train-oil flasks,
And a breaking the hoops of butter casks;
And it seemed as if a voice
(Sweeter far than by harp or by psaltery
Is breathed) called out, Oh, rats! rejoice!
The world is grown to one vast drysaltery!
To munch on, crunch on, take your nuncheon,
Breakfast, supper, dinner, luncheon!
And just as a bulky sugar puncheon,
All ready staved, like a great sun shone
Glorious scarce an inch before me,
Just as methought it said, come, bore me!
—I found the Weser rolling o'er me."

VIII

You should have heard the Hamelin people
Ringing the bells till they rocked the steeple.
  "Go," cried the Mayor, "and get long poles!
  Poke out the nests and block up the holes!
  Consult with carpenters and builders,
  And leave in our town not even a trace
  Of the rats!"—when suddenly up the face
  Of the Piper perked in the market-place,
With a, "First, if you please, my thousand guilders!"

---

tripe—*the rubbery lining of a cow's stomach that is used for food*
drysaltery—*a storage place for salted goods*
puncheon—*barrel*

IX

A thousand guilders! The Mayor looked blue;
So did the Corporation too.
For council dinners made rare havoc
With Claret, Moselle, Vin-de-Grave, Hock;
And half the money would replenish
Their cellar's biggest butt with Rhenish.
To pay this sum to a wandering fellow
With a gipsy coat of red and yellow!
   "Beside," quoth the Mayor, with a knowing wink,
   "Our business was done at the river's brink;
   We saw with our eyes the vermin sink,
   And what's dead can't come to life, I think.
   So, friend, we're not the folks to shrink
   From the duty of giving you something to drink,
   And a matter of money to put in your poke,
   But, as for the guilders, what we spoke
   Of them, as you very well know, was in joke.
   Besides, our losses have made us thrifty;
   A thousand guilders! Come, take fifty!"

X

The piper's face fell, and he cried,
"No trifling! I can't wait, beside!
I've promised to visit by dinnertime
Bagdad, and accepted the prime
Of the Head Cook's pottage, all he's rich in,
For having left the Caliph's kitchen,
Of a nest of scorpions no survivor—
With him I proved no bargain-driver,
With you, don't think I'll bate a stiver!
And folks who put me in a passion
May find me pipe to another fashion."

XI

"How?" cried the Mayor, "d'ye think I'll brook
Being worse treated than a Cook?

---

bate a stiver—*lessen by a small amount*
brook—*tolerate*

Insulted by a lazy ribald
With idle pipe and vesture piebald?
You threaten us, fellow? Do your worst,
Blow your pipe there till you burst!"

XII

Once more he stept into the street;
   And to his lips again
Laid his long pipe of smooth straight cane;
   And ere he blew three notes (such sweet
Soft notes as yet musicians cunning
   Never gave the enraptured air),
There was a rustling, that seemed like a bustling
Of merry crowds justling, at pitching and hustling,
Small feet were pattering, wooden shoes clattering,
Little hands clapping, and little tongues chattering,
And, like fowls in a farmyard when barley is scattering,
Out came the children running.
All the boys and girls,
With rosy cheeks and flaxen curls,
And sparkling eyes and teeth like pearls,
Tripping and skipping, ran merrily after
The wonderful music with shouting and laughter.

XIII

The Mayor was dumb, and the Council stood
As if they were changed into blocks of wood,
Unable to move a step, or cry
To the children merrily skipping by—
And could only follow with the eye
That joyous crowd at the Piper's back.
But how the Mayor was on the rack,
And the wretched Council's bosoms beat,
As the piper turned from the High Street
To where the Weser rolled its waters
Right in the way of their sons and daughters!

---

ribald—*a person who makes distasteful jokes*

However, he turned from South to West,
And to Koppelberg Hill his steps addressed,
And after him the children pressed;
Great was the joy in every breast.
    "He never can cross that mighty top!
    He's forced to let the piping drop
    And we shall see our children stop!"
When lo! As they reached the mountain's side,
A wondrous portal opened wide,
As if a cavern was suddenly hollowed;
And the Piper advanced and the children followed,
And when all were in to the very last,
The door in the mountain-side shut fast.
Did I say all? No! one was lame,
And could not dance the whole of the way;
And in after years, if you would blame
His sadness, he was used to say:
    "It's dull in our town since my playmates left;
    I can't forget that I'm bereft
    Of all the pleasant sights they see,
    Which the Piper also promised me;
    For he led us, he said, to a joyous land,
    Joining the town and just at hand,
Where waters gushed and fruit trees grew,
And flowers put forth a fairer hue,
And everything was strange and new.
The sparrows were brighter than peacocks here,
And their dogs outran our fallow deer,
And honey-bees had lost their stings;
And horses were born with eagle's wings;
And just as I became assured
My lame foot would be speedily cured,
The music stopped, and I stood still,
And found myself outside the Hill,
Left alone against my will,
To go now limping as before,
And never hear of that country more!"

XIV

Alas, alas for Hamelin!
    There came into many a burger's pate
    A text which says, that Heaven's Gate
Opes to the Rich at as easy rate
As the needle's eye takes a camel in!
The Mayor sent East, West, North, and South,
To offer the Piper by word of mouth,
    Wherever it was men's lot to find him,
Silver and gold to his heart's content,
If he'd only return the way he went,
    And bring the children all behind him.
But when they saw 'twas a lost endeavour,
And Piper and dancers were gone forever
They made a decree that lawyers never
    Should think their records dated duly
If, after the day of the month and year,
These words did not as well appear,
    "And so long after what happened here
    On the twenty-second of July,
    Thirteen hundred and seventy-six:"
And the better in memory to fix
The place of the Children's last retreat,
They called it, the Pied Piper's street—
Where anyone playing on pipe or tabor,
Was sure for the future to lose his labor.
Nor suffered they hostelry or tavern
To shock with mirth a street so solemn;
But opposite the place of the cavern
    They wrote the story on a column,
And on the great church window painted
The same, to make the world acquainted
How their children were stolen away;
And there it stands to this very day.
And I must not omit to say
That in Transylvania there's a tribe

---

burger's pate—*villager's head*
tabor—*a small drum*

Of alien people that ascribe
The outlandish ways and dress,
On which their neighbours lay such stress,
To their fathers and mothers having risen
Out of some subterraneous prison,
Into which they were trepanned
Long time ago in a mighty band
Out of Hamelin town in Brunswick land,
But how or why they don't understand.

XV

So, Willy, let me and you be wipers
Of scores out with all men—especially pipers!
And, whether they pipe us free from rats or from mice,
If we've promised them aught, let us keep our promise!

---

subterraneous—*underground*
trepanned—*tricked*

Time to Think

1. In what country does this story take place?
2. Why were the Mayor and the Corporation suddenly so concerned about the rats?
3. Describe the Pied Piper.
4. How did the Pied Piper use his secret charm?
5. What might have happened to the children after they left with the piper?
6. What is the moral of this story?

As Long As We Can

from Blue Willow

by Doris Gates

During the Great Depression of the 1930s, many people lost their jobs and had to look for new ways to support their families. The Larkins had moved to the Southwest, where they camped in one place after another while Mr. Larkin helped farmers plant and harvest their crops. They were able to keep few treasures from their old home besides a Bible and a china plate in a pattern called Blue Willow. To Janey, the only child, the plate symbolized a settled life and a real home. If only they could stay here at their latest stopping-place in Texas, thought Janey, especially since the lonely girl had found a friend here her own age, a dark-haired girl named Lupe Romero. For more about the hope that sustains one American family during hard times, read *Blue Willow* by Doris Gates.

When Janey returned from hanging out the washing, she found the boards of the cabin floor darkened with moisture and the smell of wet wood adding one more odor to those already filling the room. Mom was leaning a stubby broom against the wall.

Lupe Romero (lo͞o′pä rō·měr′ō)

"I couldn't do a proper job," she said frowning down at the uneven boards, "the floor's too rough. But a broom and hot suds can do a lot with elbow grease mixed with them."

Janey looked at the floor without comment. It seemed all right to her, even if Mom wasn't satisfied. Why was she always fussing about dirt? Janey wondered, irritably. As a matter of fact, Mom fussed about a good many things. Lately nothing seemed to please her. The tired look hardly ever left her face. Of course Mom would be happier if they didn't have to move about from place to place. But there wasn't anything they could do about that. Dad had to look for work wherever work happened to be, and it never lasted long in any one spot. Janey could feel herself beginning to lose patience with Mom, then remembered in time that Mom had liked Lupe. Besides, she undoubtedly meant all right, and maybe it was better to prefer cleanliness to dirt, although it was a lot more trouble.

"I might as well stir up some corndodgers as long as the oven's hot," Mrs. Larkin continued. While Janey watched, she wiped off the rickety table, produced a bowl and a small sack of yellow cornmeal and set to work. Janey eyed her speculatively. Would this be a good time for begging leave to return Lupe's call? She was nearly on the point of asking when Mom turned to her.

"As soon as I have this in the oven, we can start putting the place to rights. I can't seem to get used to living in a mess. Don't suppose I ever will, or I wouldn't mind it much by this time."

"I can untie the bedding and make up the bed," offered Janey in a small voice.

"No, it's too heavy for you. Wait till I'm through here."

Janey's neighborly inclinations strengthened.

Then, as if it were an afterthought, Mom said: "Have you done your reading yet today, Janey?"

---

corndodgers—*balls of sweet fried cornbread*
begging leave—*asking for permission to leave*

inclinations—*preferences*

"Not yet," admitted Janey. The two words seemed to put as many miles between herself and Lupe.

"Then you'd better be at it. You know what your father'd say if you let a day pass over your head without doing your stint."

Janey knew perfectly well what Dad would say if she neglected the two pages of Scripture which she was required to read daily. Dad believed there were some things second only to food and shelter in one's life. Reading was one of them.

So now Janey slid resignedly off her chair and dug to the bottom of the suitcase that held the willow plate. She lifted out a black leather-bound Book, its back and edges worn.

It didn't seem strange to her that she should be using the Bible as a textbook. It was almost the only textbook Janey had ever known. Following the harvests from place to place had left her little time for schooling, even in the camp schools provided for the use of children like her. Sometimes, as now, she wished a little wistfully that she might some day go to a "regular" school where there were plenty of books, even new books, enough for every child. It occurred to her suddenly that probably Lupe went to such a school. She had lived here a whole year. Surely she belonged by this time. Janey walked slowly back to her chair, wondering what it would be like to belong. To go to school every day, a "regular" school, week after week, month after month.

She had seen a school like that once. It was over on the coast; she didn't remember just where. They had had to stop to change a tire in front of the schoolhouse. It was a red brick schoolhouse, with white columns in front and a green lawn that stretched nearly to the road. Janey, feeling unusually daring that day, had crept up the walk until she could reach out and touch the smooth white columns. Glancing back at the car, she had made sure that her father and mother were still busy with the

---

stint—*time spent doing a job*   resignedly—*with an attitude of submission*

tire. And then she had edged along the building, her clothes brushing against the rough bricks until she was able to peep into a window. Inside was a room full of boys and girls. Some were sitting at desks, others were writing at the blackboard, and all of them looked as if they belonged. For a long time Janey stood there watching, until a shout from the car sent her speeding back along the way she had come. It is doubtful if any in the schoolroom had known they were being spied upon.

Yes, it would be nice to go to such a school. She wished she were there now. It would be lots more fun than sitting here in a stifling room, poring over tiny print full of "thee's" and "thou's" and words her tongue stumbled over when she asked their meaning. Still, she had learned to read by this strange method, and she supposed it would be a very good thing to know how to read if she should suddenly find herself in a district school, though goodness only knew how that would ever come about. And then, besides that, there were undoubtedly good stories in the Bible. Very good stories indeed. Daniel in the lions' den, and Noah's Ark, for instance.

She decided she would read about the Ark and the Flood today. It was a good time to read about a rain that lasted forty days and forty nights. It might help as much as the blue plate to lift the weight of the heat.

Perching herself on the chair and hooking her bare heels over its rungs, she opened the worn, black Book and began to read. Now and then she would put her fingers on a word to fasten it to the page until she had sounded it out. No matter how many times she read the chapter, those strange names always caused her to hesitate a little.

The oven door had slammed shut on the corn bread and Mrs. Larkin had gone outside for a breath of what might be considered cooler air before Janey came to the last verse.

> While the earth remaineth, seedtime and harvest, and cold and heat, and summer and winter, and day and night shall not cease.

She closed the Book and squeezed it between the two
patches that covered her knees. Her hands stroked the soft
leather in a thoughtful way. There was really nothing to be
worried about, she decided, thinking of that last verse and of
Mom's fussing. God had promised that there would always be
harvests, so Dad would always have something to do. While
the earth remaineth. And even the hot weather couldn't last
forever. Winter would have to come along some day. And there
was the blue plate. Now, if only Mom didn't look quite so sad,
and if only she, Janey, could go to a "regular" school, the world
wouldn't have much the matter with it, she thought. And as if to
prove it, she heard Mom say just at that moment: "You can run
over to Lupe's for a while if you want."

It was sundown before Mr. Larkin came home. The shack
had been settled for hours, the bed made, the suitcase shoved out
of sight underneath it, while corndodgers reposed in state in the
middle of the table.

Once again, Janey was sitting on the top step to greet her
father as soon as he should come into sight. Away off on the
western edge of the world, a red and angry sun was being swal-

---

reposed—*rested*

lowed up in its own heat waves. It was nearly gone now, and the faintest hint of a breeze was beginning to stir a single hair here and there on Janey's tousled towhead. If only the wind would really make up its mind to blow, to blow good and hard and send this dead hot air ahead of it out of the valley, or at least to some other part of it! she thought.

And then a battered car came into sight up the road, and Janey, with a cry over her shoulder, "It's Dad!" was off the step in a bound and down to the road. She trotted along beside the car as it bumped across the uneven ground to the house—the heat, Mom's tired face, and even Lupe forgotten in this moment's joy. Dad was home again!

"Hi, young one," Mr. Larkin called as he slowly eased himself from behind the wheel. "Shouldn't run like that on a hot day. Your face's as red as a cock's comb."

Janey smiled happily and pressed close to him as he reached into the car and lifted out some parcels.

"Here," he said, "take these in to your mother while I lift out the cushion on the back seat."

Janey took the bundles into the house, and presently her father appeared with the cushion to the back seat gripped awkwardly in his arms.

"Where do you want this?" he asked.

"Doesn't matter now," his wife answered. "When Janey goes to bed we'll put it across one of the doors. It'll be cooler."

For this was to be Janey's bed tonight as it had been for many, many nights before this one. In fact, Janey wouldn't have known how to sleep on anything else. It was all the bed she knew, and she found it entirely satisfactory in every way. Of course, now that she was ten, her feet stuck out over the end of it a little, but the suitcase, shoved across the end, solved this difficulty.

---

towhead—*a head of white-blond hair*

"Will the job last very long, Dad?" Janey wanted to know.

"Can't say exactly. More than likely, though. We'll keep on irrigating for a while, and when picking starts I can't see any reason why I shouldn't get in on that too. You never come to the end of work in a cotton patch, Janey."

"What's the pay?" Mrs. Larkin asked.

"Two bits an hour, and I worked eight hours. How much is that, daughter? Quick now."

He whirled on Janey and stood grinning while she turned over in her mind this problem in mental arithmetic. She fastened her eyes on his as if she thought she could read the answer there. And just when the grin was broadening accusingly, "Two dollars!" shouted Janey, as quick as that.

"Correct," said her father, beaming. "That's a right pert child we're rearing under our roof."

"There are times when I'm glad it isn't our roof, like now," Mom returned, and walked heavily to the table where the parcels which held their supper lay alongside the corndodgers.

"It isn't much to brag about, and that's a fact," Mr. Larkin agreed, looking critically around him, "but it sure looks a sight better than it did this morning before you took it over."

Mom did smile at this, and Mr. Larkin, much encouraged, added in a teasing voice: "It must be awful to love to scrub as much as you do, Clara, and then never have a house worth scrubbing. Maybe it'll be different some day."

"Maybe," she returned briefly, the smile gone.

For a moment Mr. Larkin looked at her, his face suddenly sad and his shoulders drooping. Then he turned to Janey.

"Come on, young one. We'd better rustle up some more firewood before it gets dark."

Side by side, the two figures, one very tall, the other very short, both clad in faded blue overalls, moved slowly over the

---

two bits—*twenty-five cents*   pert—*lively*

plain back of the shack. Each of them dragged a gunnysack, and
into these they poked whatever pieces of grease-wood branches
or roots they could find. When the sacks were filled, Mr. Larkin
took one in either hand and dragged them up to the back door.
Then he and Janey took the water pail and went with it to the
windmill in the neighboring field. It was necessary to open a
gate strung with barbed wire in order to enter the field.

There were cattle in that field, large, red beasts that jogged
away awkwardly and stood staring at the strangers as they
opened the gate.

Janey hesitated.

"These steers won't bother us any. Not like real range
cattle," Dad said, and Janey, apparently reassured, walked boldly
beside him. Secretly, however, she was still a little apprehensive
and regarded the cattle with suspicion.

"Lupe Romero from across the road came over today," Janey
said while they waited for the bucket to fill. "She says the house
we're in belongs to the man who owns this windmill and these
cattle."

---

gunnysack—*a bag made of heavy, coarse material*   apprehensive—*uneasy*
range cattle—*cattle that roam freely on open plains*

"Yes, I know," returned Mr. Larkin. "Her father told me this morning when I went over there."

"Does he know we're living in his house?" queried Janey.

"As far as I know he doesn't."

They were on the way back to the shack now. Janey closed the gate, then ran to catch up with her father, who had gone on ahead with the brimming bucket.

"Suppose he won't let us stay when he finds out; what will we do then?" she asked, a strange fear all at once seizing her. Suppose they should have to go away tomorrow or next day? She might never see Lupe again!

Mr. Larkin stopped and looked over her head to the west and thought a moment before replying. Janey searched his face anxiously.

"He'd probably let us stay if we paid him something every month. I'd rather do that than move to the cotton camp. We'd have to pay rent there anyway, and we're better off by ourselves, Janey, even if we have to do without some things in order to stay that way."

Janey nodded her head in quick agreement.

"The Romeros have stayed in their house for a year. Do you think he'd let us stay that long?"

"If we paid up, he probably would."

Suddenly a strange tingling began to creep all over Janey, and her chest felt all at once too small for what was going on inside of it. Perhaps they wouldn't have to move on after a month or so! Perhaps Dad was going to stay put, and she and Lupe could become real friends. She might even go to school wherever Lupe did. A "regular" school, not just a camp school for roving children.

Before she could gather her wits for a proper reply, her father was speaking again. "We'll have to call a halt somewhere pretty soon, Janey. Mom isn't well, hasn't been for a long time. Maybe if she could stay long enough somewhere to get a real good rest, it would make a difference with her. It's hard to say, though."

"Then we'll stay as long as we can?" Janey asked.

"Yes, as long as we can."

Janey sighed and her bare toes dragged a little as she followed Dad to the house. It was the same old question and the same old answer. What wouldn't she give to be able to say just once: "We'll stay as long as we want to"!

When they got inside, they found supper ready for them. By moving the table over to the bed, there were seats enough for all three. After the dishes were washed, they sat on the front steps until bedtime. The little breeze had strengthened, and the moon was lighting earth and sky with a radiance that was like balm to eyes still smarting from too brilliant sunlight. From the top of a pole at the road's edge, a mockingbird dropped three notes as silvery as the moon's own light.

"'While the earth remaineth, seedtime and harvest, and cold and heat, and summer and winter, and day and night shall not cease,'" Janey remembered thankfully.

Across the road a light twinkled in the Romero house.

"And there's Lupe as long as we do stay," thought Janey with equal gratitude.

Character Theme—Contentment

Time to Think

1. Why did the Larkin family have to move so often? What did this moving prevent Janey from doing?
2. How did Janey learn?
3. What two possessions made Janey feel at home even though they moved from house to house?
4. Why was Lupe Romero important to Janey?

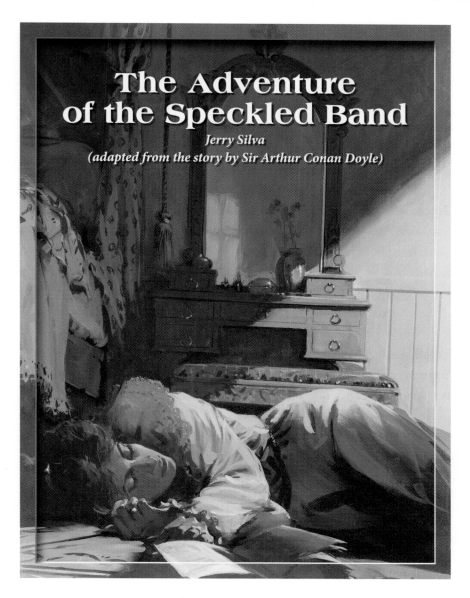

The Adventure of the Speckled Band

Jerry Silva
(adapted from the story by Sir Arthur Conan Doyle)

CHARACTERS

JULIA STONER
HELEN STONER, *her sister*
DR. GRIMESLY ROYLOTT, *their stepfather*
INSPECTOR LESTRADE
LIEUTENANT KELLY
DR. BURNWELL
SHERLOCK HOLMES
DR. WATSON

SCENE 1

TIME: *1874.*

SETTING: *A bedroom, appropriately furnished with bed, night table and two chairs. There is a bellpull near the bed, and a ventilator near the top of the bellpull.*

AT RISE: *The room is dark. JULIA is in bed. There is a hissing sound, and she bolts upright.*

JULIA: What's that? Is anyone there? *(Suddenly she screams, and jumps out of bed. She yells.)* The speckled band! The speckled band! *(She staggers a few steps and collapses. A soft but high-pitched whistle is heard, then the clanging of metal on metal. Curtain.)*

SCENE 2

TIME: *A while later.*

SETTING: *Same as Scene 1, except the bedroom is lighted.*

AT RISE: *JULIA's body lies on floor, covered with sheet. HELEN is seated on bed, weeping into handkerchief. LESTRADE and DR. BURNWELL stand center, talking.*

LESTRADE: Dr. Burnwell, can you determine the cause of Miss Stoner's death?

BURNWELL: Inspector Lestrade, I can't find a mark on this girl's body. It's extraordinary!

LESTRADE: Could she have been poisoned?

BURNWELL: She has none of the outward signs of poisoning, though I can't be sure until after the autopsy.

LESTRADE *(Turning to HELEN):* Easy, my dear, take it easy. I must ask you a few questions for the record. *(Takes out small notebook and pencil.)*

HELEN *(Composing herself):* All right. Go ahead.

LESTRADE: What is your full name?

---

bellpull—*a cord that is attached to a servant's bell*
ventilator—*a device that allows air to circulate*
autopsy—*the medical examination of a dead body to find the cause of death*

HELEN: Helen Margaret Stoner.

LESTRADE: Your age?

HELEN: Twenty.

LESTRADE: Your sister's full name was . . . ?

HELEN: Julia Jean Stoner.

LESTRADE: Her age?

HELEN: Twenty, also. We were twins.

LESTRADE: How many people live in this house?

HELEN: My stepfather, Dr. Grimesly Roylott, and I, and *(Starts crying)* . . . Julia.

LESTRADE: Now, now, just a few more questions. *(Pauses)* Are you sure you heard a whistle last night after your sister screamed?

HELEN: Yes. In fact, I have heard it the last few nights. It puzzled me, but I could not determine its cause.

LESTRADE: How about the metallic sound? Are you sure you heard it?

HELEN: Yes, I'm sure.

LESTRADE: What do you think your sister meant by "the speckled band"?

HELEN: I really can't imagine. *(LIEUTENANT KELLY enters.)*

LESTRADE *(To KELLY)*: Just a minute, Lieutenant Kelly. *(To HELEN)* All right, Miss Stoner, you may leave. Thank you for your help. *(She exits.)*

BURNWELL: There's nothing more I can do here, Inspector. I'll let you know if there's any evidence of poisoning . . . though at this point, it doesn't look like it.

LESTRADE: All right, Dr. Burnwell. Keep me informed. Good day.

BURNWELL: Good day. *(He exits.)*

LESTRADE *(Crossing to chair and sitting)*: Well, Lieutenant Kelly, what's your report?

KELLY: I have gone over this room inside and out with a fine-toothed comb, and I can find absolutely no evidence to support a crime. The windows were all locked, the door was locked, and the key was still in the lock on the inside.

LESTRADE: Yes, I know. When I first arrived I had to break the lock of the door to get in.

KELLY: It is my opinion that Miss Stoner had to have been alone all night.

LESTRADE: But how and why did she die?

KELLY: Maybe from fright, sir, pure and simple.

LESTRADE: What could she have been so afraid of?

KELLY: I don't know, sir. However, I did notice a band of gypsies down the road about a mile.

LESTRADE: So?

KELLY: Well, they wear spotted handkerchiefs around their heads. Perhaps that is what Miss Stoner meant when she cried "the speckled band."

LESTRADE: Yes, it's possible.

KELLY: One of them may have come to the house to steal, and she may have seen him at the window.

LESTRADE: And it frightened her to death.

KELLY: Yes.

LESTRADE: That is one theory. There's one thing that puzzles me, though—I don't think a twenty-year-old heart would stop out of fright.

KELLY: What should we do? What leads are there to follow?

LESTRADE: None. We have no evidence of crime, no cause of death, no motive for murder, and no suspects.

KELLY: Do you think we should advise the victim's sister to call *him* in, sir?

LESTRADE: By "him" you can mean only one man.

KELLY: Yes, she must call in . . . (LESTRADE *and* KELLY *turn to face the audience)*

LESTRADE and **KELLY** *(Together):* Sherlock Holmes. *(Curtain)*

SCENE 3

SETTING: *Sherlock Holmes's office. It is appropriately furnished with desk, chairs, and armchair of the Victorian period. There is fireplace on backdrop.*

AT RISE: HOLMES *is sitting in armchair, reading a newspaper. There is a knock at the door.*

HOLMES: Come in. (HELEN *enters.* HOLMES *rises, extends his hand.*) Good morning. Miss Stoner, I presume?

HELEN *(Shaking his hand):* Yes.

HOLMES: Inspector Lestrade informed me that you would be coming. *(Indicating chair)* Please sit down. Would you like a cup of hot coffee? I see that you are shivering.

HELEN *(Sitting):* It is not cold that makes me shiver.

HOLMES: What, then?

HELEN: It is fear, Mr. Holmes. It is terror.

HOLMES: Now, you must not fear. Matters shall soon be set right, I have no doubt. You have come in by train this morning, I see.

HELEN *(Puzzled):* How do you know that?

HOLMES: I observed the second half of a return ticket in the palm of your left glove. You must have started early, and yet you had a good drive in a dog-cart, along heavy roads, before you reached the station.

HELEN *(Staring at* HOLMES*):* How do you know?

HOLMES: There is no mystery, madam. The left arm of your jacket is spattered with mud in no less than seven places. The marks are fresh. There is no vehicle but a dog-cart which throws up mud in that way and then only when one sits on the left-hand side of the driver.

HELEN: Whatever your reasons may be, you are perfectly correct. (WATSON *enters.*)

WATSON: Oh, excuse me, Holmes. I didn't realize you were with someone. *(Turns to leave)*

---

dog-cart—*a two-wheeled cart drawn by one horse*

297

HOLMES: No, come in, come in. Miss Stoner, this is my intimate friend and associate, Dr. Watson.

WATSON *(Extending his hand):* How do you do, Miss Stoner. Inspector Lestrade has told us of your sister's death. My condolences.

HELEN: Thank you, Dr. Watson.

HOLMES: Miss Stoner, Dr. Watson has helped me clear up many a mystery, and I would like him to stay and listen to your story. Inspector Lestrade has told us as much as he can of the mysterious death of your sister. *(WATSON sits.)* Now, I'd like you to tell me a little of your family history.

HELEN: I am living with my stepfather, Dr. Grimesly Roylott, who is the last survivor of one of the oldest families in England—the Roylotts of Stoke Moran.

HOLMES: Yes, I am familiar with the name.

HELEN: The Roylott family was at one time among the richest in England. However, their fortune was squandered in the last century by the few remaining heirs. My stepfather was left practically penniless, but was able to earn a medical degree. He then went to Calcutta, India, to practice.

HOLMES: Was he successful?

HELEN: For a while. There were some robberies in his house, and in a fit of anger he beat his butler to death. He suffered a long imprisonment and returned to England a disappointed man.

HOLMES: When did he marry your mother?

HELEN: While he was in India. My twin sister and I were only two years old at the time. My mother left a considerable amount of money when she died, and it is her money that supports the household now.

HOLMES: It was left to Dr. Roylott?

HELEN: Well, yes and no. According to the will he receives one thousand pounds a year from the bank. We,

---

condolences—*expressions of sympathy*   squandered—*wasted*

298

that is Julia and I, receive a small allowance that is enough to live on. If we marry or move away, each of us receives a third of the inheritance, however.

HOLMES: Tell me more of your stepfather.

HELEN: He is a man of immense strength and uncontrollable anger. Since he returned to England he has been involved in a series of brawls. Last week, he threw the local blacksmith over a parapet into a stream.

HOLMES *(With raised eyebrows):* Indeed? Now, Miss Stoner, you said when you came in that you were afraid. Can you explain your fears?

HELEN: No—somehow just being in the house causes me to be afraid.

HOLMES: I see. You have acted wisely in seeking my help. Have you told me everything?

HELEN: Yes, all.

HOLMES: Miss Stoner, I don't believe you have. You are protecting your stepfather.

HELEN: Why, what do you mean?

HOLMES *(Walking over to her and pushing up the sleeve of her blouse):* Your arm is badly bruised, Miss Stoner. You have been cruelly treated.

HELEN *(Withdrawing her hand):* He is a hard man. Perhaps he does not know his own strength.

HOLMES: This is a very serious business. There are a thousand details I wish to know, Miss Stoner. If we were to come to Stoke Moran today, would it be possible for us to see the house without your stepfather's knowledge?

HELEN: As it happens, he spoke of coming to town today on business. There should be no one there to disturb you.

HOLMES: Excellent. Till then, Miss Stoner.

HELEN *(Rising):* Good day, Mr. Holmes. *(To* WATSON*)* You too, Dr. Watson.

---

parapet—*a low wall on the edge of a bridge*

Holmes: Good day.

Watson (*Showing her to door*): Good day. (*She exits.*)

Holmes: Watson, my friend, what do you think?

Watson: It is a most dark and sinister business. According to Lestrade, the victim must have been alone. There seems not a clue as to how she died.

Holmes: On the contrary, Watson. There are many clues— maybe too many.

Watson: We'll go over them. I would be much interested in your theory. I should think—(*There is a loud banging at the door, and* DR. ROYLOTT *walks quickly into room.*)

Roylott: Which of you is Holmes?

Holmes: I am, sir.

Roylott: I am Dr. Grimesly Roylott of Stoke Moran.

Holmes: Indeed, doctor. (*Indicating chair*) Take a seat.

Roylott: I will do nothing of the kind. My stepdaughter has been here. I have traced her. What has she been saying to you?

Holmes: It is a little cold for this time of year, don't you agree?

Roylott (*Loudly*): What has she been saying to you?

Holmes: I have heard that the marigolds promise well.

Roylott: Ha, you put me off, do you? (*Steps forward, shaking his fist*) I know you, you scoundrel! I have heard of you before. You are Holmes the meddler.

Holmes: Some people say that.

Roylott (*Stepping closer to* HOLMES): Holmes the busybody!

Holmes: That, too.

Roylott (*Stepping face to face with* HOLMES): Holmes, the Scotland Yard jack-in-the box!

Holmes (*Chuckling*): Your conversation is most entertaining. When you go out, close the door—there is a decided draft.

---

sinister—*evil*

Roylott *(Backing off):* I will go when I have had my say. Don't meddle in my affairs. I am a dangerous man to cross. *(He grabs a poker and bends it with his hands.)* See that you stay out of my grip. *(He throws the poker down and strides out.)*

Holmes *(Rising and going over to poker):* Seems a very likable person. I am not so big, but if he had remained, I might have shown him that my grip is no less than his own. *(He picks up the poker and bends it back.)* Imagine his confusing me with Scotland Yard! How ridiculous! *(Pauses)* Watson, let's go, the game's afoot! *(HOLMES and WATSON reach for their coats and exit as the curtain closes.)*

⌒ SCENE 4 ⌒

Setting: *Same as Scene 2.*

At Rise: *As curtain opens,* HELEN *enters, followed by* HOLMES *and* WATSON.

Helen: This is Julia's room.

Holmes: Yes, much as Lestrade described it to me. *(HOLMES takes quick walk around the room.)* Miss Stoner, we have had the pleasure of making Dr. Roylott's acquaintance.

Helen: Good heavens! Did he follow me?

Holmes: So it appears.

Helen: He is so cunning. I never know when I am safe. What will he say when he returns?

Holmes: He must guard himself, for he may find that someone more cunning is on his track.

Watson: Do not fear, Miss Stoner. Mr. Holmes will make sure nothing happens to you. *(He sneezes.)*

Holmes: Where is Dr. Roylott's room, Miss Stoner?

Helen: Next to this one. Do you suspect him?

Holmes: May I see his room? *(WATSON sneezes again.)*

---

afoot—*happening; being carried on*

HELEN: Why, yes. The door is open.

HOLMES: Very good. While I look around Dr. Roylott's room, Watson, would you please ask Miss Stoner about the animals in this house?

HELEN: How did you know that there are animals here? You have seen none.

HOLMES *(As he is leaving):* Dr. Watson is unfortunately allergic to most animal fur, as you can see. *(WATSON sneezes again as HOLMES exits.)*

HELEN: Yes, Dr. Watson, my stepfather keeps a cheetah and a baboon in the house.

WATSON: Why? Those are odd animals for pets.

HELEN: If you remember, he first practiced medicine in India. He brought the animals back with him.

WATSON: Where does he keep them?

HELEN: Actually, he lets them wander at will over the grounds. They are tame, but the neighbors fear them almost as much as they fear the doctor himself.

WATSON: I am beginning to see why you don't enjoy living in this house. The goings-on are strange indeed. *(HOLMES re-enters.)*

HOLMES: Watson, have you found anything in here?

WATSON: Everything seems to be in order. Miss Stoner has told me—

HOLMES: I know what she has told you. I heard her through the ventilator.

WATSON: Oh.

HOLMES: Does that strike you as strange?

WATSON: Uh, no . . . no, I guess not.

HOLMES: Oh, come, my dear Watson. What kind of ventilator ventilates into the next room rather than to the outside, as it should?

WATSON *(Musing):* Yes. Come to think of it, they should not be built that way.

HOLMES: I wonder if there is anything else that has been passed over? *(He takes magnifying glass from pocket* *and starts to examine the floor near the bed and a few objects on the night table.)*

WATSON: Surely, Holmes, that is not of importance.

HOLMES: One never knows. Miss Stoner, why is the bed clamped to the floor?

HELEN: Why, I don't know. The bed in my room isn't. *(HOLMES continues to examine objects in the room, including the bell rope.)*

HOLMES: This bellpull, Miss Stoner. I assume it is to call a maid. Do you have one?

HELEN: No. We can't afford a maid.

HOLMES: Have you or your sister ever used it?

HELEN: No. Anything we needed we got for ourselves.

HOLMES: Would you try it now, Miss Stoner?

HELEN *(Pulling it):* Why, it's a dummy! *(Looking up at ventilator)* No wonder it doesn't ring! It's not even attached to a wire. It's fastened to a hook just above the opening of the ventilator.

HOLMES: That's right. It serves no function whatsoever. *(Reflectively)* Or so it would seem. *(Pauses)* Miss Stoner, this room looks as if it's being prepared for someone. Is it?

HELEN: Why, yes. I am going to sleep here for a few nights. My stepfather is having iron bars put across my windows as added protection. I will be sleeping in this room meanwhile.

HOLMES: If you do so, Miss Stoner, your life will be in the utmost danger.

HELEN: But—but why, Mr. Holmes?

HOLMES: I prefer to keep my suspicions to myself until I have clearer proof. What I want you to do tonight, however, is to come to this room as if you were going to bed. Watson and I will be waiting outside the window. You will leave by the window and spend the night in town, and we will take your place here.

HELEN: Well, it all seems very strange, Mr. Holmes.

HOLMES: You must trust us, my dear. Will you do it?

HELEN: Very well, I will.

HOLMES: Fine. I'll see you tonight at about ten o'clock. Watson and I would like to look around here for another few minutes, if you don't mind.

HELEN: Feel free to stay as long as you like. Good day, gentlemen.

HOLMES: Good day.

WATSON: Good day, Miss Stoner. *(HELEN exits.)*

HOLMES: Watson, can you guess what I found in Dr. Roylott's room?

WATSON: Come now, Holmes, how can I possibly know?

HOLMES: My dear Watson, I found exactly what I expected to find—a safe. I also found a saucer of milk on the floor. Have you seen any cats around this house?

WATSON: No. I can't imagine why Dr. Roylott would have that in his room.

HOLMES: I also found a dog whip with a loop tied at the end of it.

WATSON *(Getting angry):* So what? I don't understand this entire case. A speckled band, whistles and clangs in the night, beds bolted to the floor, dummy bellpulls, ventilators that don't ventilate, and now a dog whip, a saucer of milk, and a safe in a man's bedroom. What does it all add up to?

HOLMES: Murder, my dear Watson, it all adds up to murder. *(Curtain)*

⌐ **SCENE 5** ⌐

SETTING: *Same as Scene 4, except room is dark.*

AT RISE: HOLMES *stands near ventilator, staring at it and listening intently.* WATSON *is in chair, asleep.*

HOLMES *(Whispering):* Watson. *(There is no answer. HOLMES whispers louder.)* Watson! Watson, are you awake?

WATSON *(Waking up with a start; speaking in normal voice):* What! *(Whispers)* Oh, yes. Yes, of course.

HOLMES: Stay awake, Watson. Your life may depend on it. *(A few seconds pass with no sound, then there is a loud click offstage. HOLMES looks quickly and hard at the ventilator. There is a hiss. He whispers.)* Did you hear that hissing sound? *(There is another, louder hiss. HOLMES speaks very loudly.)* Quickly, Watson, a light! (WATSON *runs over to get a candle.* HOLMES *is whacking at bellpull and ventilator with a cane.)* Hi-ya! Hi-ya! *(A loud, high-pitched whistle is heard three times in succession. Then* ROYLOTT *screams from offstage.* WATSON *starts to run out, but* HOLMES *stops him.)* Don't go into Roylott's room, Watson. Just close his door immediately. I suspect Roylott is dead by now.

WATSON *(Hesitating):* What?

HOLMES: Quickly, man! (WATSON *runs offstage. The sound of a door being shut is heard.* HOLMES *lights the candle.* WATSON *walks back in, obviously shaken.)*

WATSON *(Shakily):* It was a snake, Holmes! There is a snake in that room.

HOLMES: A yellow one with brown speckles, I presume.

WATSON: That's right! The speckled band! That's what Julia meant. In the dark it must have looked like a speckled band!

HOLMES: Most assuredly, Watson. It is a swamp adder, an extremely poisonous snake from India. No doubt I aroused its temper when I hit it with my cane, and it bit the first person it saw—Dr. Roylott.

WATSON: The saucer of milk must have been its food. The snake was kept in the safe and the dog whip with the loop was used to carry the snake from the safe to the ventilator!

HOLMES: Correct, my dear Watson.

WATSON: Yes, I see now. The snake squirmed through the ventilator, across the fake bellpull, and dropped down upon its victim in the bed.

HOLMES: Which is why . . .

WATSON: Which is why the bed is clamped to the floor! No one could move it away from the bellpull.

HOLMES: Also correct.

WATSON: What about the clangs and whistles?

HOLMES: Come now, Watson. The clangs were caused by the closing of the safe. The whistle was used to call the snake back into the other room after it had done its evil work in this one.

WATSON: What can it all mean?

HOLMES: It means it's all over for Dr. Roylott. He will inherit nothing now. He was trying to kill his stepdaughters for their money. If they had married, he would have had a mere pittance.

WATSON: Of course, it is so clear now. Why couldn't I see it before?

HOLMES: You did see it, Watson, but you did not understand it. You had all the pieces but could not then solve the puzzle. Actually this room was loaded with clues. Well, come along now, Watson, we must see Inspector Lestrade. *(They start walking offstage.)*

WATSON *(Still astounded):* Amazing!

HOLMES: Elementary, my dear Watson, elementary. *(Curtain)*

---

pittance—*a very small amount of money*

Character Theme—Justice

Time to Think

1. What are the only clues that Helen can give Inspector Lestrade about her sister's death?
2. What did Lieutenant Kelly report of his inspection of the premises?
3. How does Holmes reveal his keen powers of deduction when he meets Helen Stoner?
4. Julia's room was loaded with clues, but only Holmes could see their significance. What were the clues?
5. What was the speckled band?
6. What prompted Dr. Roylett's evil plan?

Credits